Physiology
Review & Assessment

MCQs, Case based MCQs, Viva/Short Questions

Dr. Gopal Krushna Pal, MD, PhD, DSc
Executive Director & CEO
AIIMS Patna & AIIMS Gorakhpur

Co-Authors

Pravati Pal
MBBS, MD, MABMS, BNYT, MD (AM)
Professor, Department of Physiology, JIPMER, Puducherry, India

Nivedita Nanda
MSc, PhD (Medical Biochemistry), BNYT
Additional Professor, Department of Biochemistry, JIPMER, Puducherry, India.

ELSEVIER

AHUJA'S
AHUJA PUBLISHING HOUSE
KNOWLEDGE YOU NEED. CALIBRE YOU DESERVE

ELSEVIER

RELX India Pvt. Ltd.
Registered Office: 818, Indraprakash Building,
8th Floor, 21, Barakhamba Road, New Delhi-110001
Corporate Office: 14th Floor, Building No. 10B,
DLF Cyber City, Phase II, Gurgaon-122002, Haryana, India

AHUJA'S
Ahuja Publishing House

Ahuja Publishing House
Registered Office:
C-8/124 B Lawrence road,
Delhi-110035, India

Physiology: Review & Assessment (MCQs, Case Based MCQs, Viva/Short Questions), GK Pal

ISBN: 978-81-312-7086-8
e-Book ISBN: 978-81-312-7087-5

This *Physiology: Review & Assessment (MCQs, Case Based MCQs, Viva/Short Questions)*, by GK Pal is co-published by arrangement with RELX India Pvt. Ltd. and Ahuja Publishing House.

Printed at: S.K. Offset Shahdara India

SECTION I - GENERAL PHYSIOLOGY

MULTIPLE CHOICE QUESTIONS

1. Junctions between cells in membranes either allow the transfer of molecules or prevent transfer of molecules. These junctions are of three types:
   Tight junctions that prevent transfer of substances
   Adhering junctions that maintain cellular positions
   Gap junctions that allow movement of substances.
   Which of the below is a characteristic of gap (communicating) junctions?
   A. Allow small molecules to pass from the inside to the outside of a cell
   B. Allow small molecules to pass from the inside of one cell to another
   C. Are impermeable to ions
   D. Are present in the blood–brain barrier
   E. Are absent in the cornea.

2. A 35-year-old woman has thyrotoxicosis. Her thyroid-stimulating hormone (TSH) is very low. What is the physiological mechanism that caused the reduction in this patient's TSH?
   A. Autonomous control
   B. Counter-current control
   C. Desensitization
   D. Negative feedback
   E. Positive feedback

3. An artificial membrane is created with a lipid bilayer without protein molecules in the membrane. The lipid composition of the membrane is essentially the same as that of a normal biological membrane. To which of the following substances is the membrane more permeable than to water molecules?
   A. Carbon dioxide B. Glucose C. Glycerol
   D. Fructose E. Urea

4. Cells in the human body require adenosine triphosphate (ATP) for energy. ATP is produced primarily through the Krebs cycle (tricarboxylic acid cycle) and the electron transport chain system. Oxygen is the ultimate acceptor of the electron transport chain. Without it, the tricarboxylic acid cycle and the electron transport chain are abruptly interrupted and, with it, the production of ATP as well. Without ATP, sodium/potassium pumps do not work, cells begin to swell, and membranes begin to depolarize and become electrically unstable. This is manifested in convulsions, arrhythmias and muscle cramps. In which part of the cell is the electron transport chain located?
   A. Golgi apparatus
   B. Smooth endoplasmic reticulum
   C. Rough endoplasmic reticulum
   D. Centrioles
   E. Mitochondria

5. The equilibrium potentials of Na, K and Cl are presented. $ENa^+ = +61mV$ $EK^+ = -94mV$ $ECl^- = -72mV$ If it is accepted that a cell is permeable to these three ions and has a resting membrane potential of −85 mV, which of the following combinations best describes the movement of ions through the cell membrane by passive diffusion? Sodium Potassium Chloride Option 1 Inward Inward Inward Option 2 Inward Inward Outward Option 3 Inward Outward Inward Option 4 Inward Outward Outward Option 5 Outward Inward Inward Option 6 Outward Inward Outward Option 7 Outward Outward Inward Option 8 Outward Outward Outward
   A. Option A B. Option B C. Option C
   D. Option D E. Option E F. Option F
   G. Option G H. Option H

6. In order for a cell to live, grow and reproduce, it must be able to obtain nutrients from its environment. There are several mechanisms by which this ingestion occurs. Match the following description with the corresponding mechanism from the following list of cellular transport mechanisms. The carrying of a substance through the membrane by a physical protein structure that penetrates all the way through the membrane is known as what?
   A. Diffusion **B. Active transport**
   C. Endocytosis D. Pinocytosis
   E. Phagocytosis

7. Human cell-to-cell communication occurs through signalling mechanisms requiring a signalling molecule and a receptor molecule that produces an effect in the target cell; the effector. Extracellular chemical messengers are ligands that bind to cell surface receptors to exert intracellular effects. Common examples of the mechanisms for extracellular chemical messengers to exert intracellular effects include:
   A. Inhibition of cytoplasmic receptors to start transcription of specific mRNA
   B. Opening ion channels in the cell membrane
   C. Direct entry into the nucleus to start transcription of specific mRNA
   D. Inducing altered electrical potential inside the cell
   E. Binding to nuclear receptors to initiate release of intracellular messengers

8. A 42-year-old woman decides to lose weight on a diet prescribed by an anorexic friend. She loses about 15 kilos in 45 days, but her serum potassium decreases to 2.1 mmol/L (normal: 3,5 to 5 mmol/L). Which of the following changes is most likely in this young woman?
   A. Depolarization of membrane potential at rest
   B. Hyperpolarization of membrane potential at rest
   C. Increased intracellular potassium concentration
   D. The potassium potential in equilibrium is less negative
   E. Increased extracellular potassium concentration

9. A 22-year-old male enters the emergency department after a traffic accident. He hasn't lost much blood, but he has severe crushing trauma to his right leg. He's conscious and shows flaccid paralysis. The electrocardiogram shows a shortened QT interval and increased P-R interval (i.e. decreased duration of action potential and decreased driving speed). Analysis shows that his serum potassium has increased to a value of 6.5 mEq/L (normal: 3.5 to 5 mEq/L). Which of the following effects does this increase in serum potassium cause?
   A. Decrease in the net force for the movement of potassium from the cells
   B. Decreased intracellular potassium concentration
   C. Hyperpolarization of membrane potential at rest
   D. Nernst's most negative potential for potassium
   E. More negative membrane resting potential

10. An 88-year-old man who lives in a nursing home and has diabetes mellitus is taking diuretics for his hypertension. Recently, blood glucose was higher than 350 mg/dL. He is disoriented and in the last five days his oral intake has been scarce. His vital signs are 38.1 ºC, a blood pressure of 150/90 mmHg and a pulse of 100 lpm in supine decubitus, as well as a blood pressure of 130/88 mmHg and a pulse of 118 lpm in standing. The results of the heart scan are normal and his armpits are dry. The table shows the serum Na^+ and K^+ values before and after the dehydration that developed in this patient. The resting membrane potential of a cardiac myocyte was about −70 millivolts before dehydration. What is the resting membrane potential of a cardiac myocyte after dehydration, assuming no change in membrane conductance or intracellular concentrations of Na^+ or K^+? Before After Na^+ serum 140 mmol/L 151 mmol/L K^+ serum 3,5 mmol/L 3,5 mmol/L
    A. −100 millivolts
    B. −50 millivolts
    C. −60 millivolts
    D. −72 millivolts
    E. −90 millivolts

11. A 44-year-old male is recovering from third-degree burns to more than 50% of his body surface. He has a low serum potassium concentration (2.9 mEq/L). He displays postural hypotension and skeletal muscle weakness. If the equilibrium potential of K^+ in a neuron is −105 mV and the equilibrium potential of Na^+ is +55 mV, what would be the approximate value of the resting membrane potential of a neuron in this patient?
    A. +20 millivolts
    B. +48 millivolts
    C. +80 millivolts
    D. −25 mV
    E. −48 mV
    F. −96 mV

12. A 23-year-old male suffers a traffic accident with crushing of his right leg. Serum potassium concentration is 6.4 mEq/L. The equilibrium potential of K^+ in a motor neuron is −73 mV, and the equilibrium potential of Na^+ is +59 mV. Which of the following values describes the resting membrane potential (in mV) of this patient's normal motor neuron?
    A. +62
    B. +90
    C. −13
    D. −67
    E. −84

13. A 63-year-old male suffers dehydration after three days of heavy alcohol consumption. Serum sodium has increased from a normal value of 140 mEq/L to 147 mEq/L. The resting membrane potential of a normal neuron was 80 mV before dehydration. What is the most likely resting membrane potential of a normal neuron after dehydration, assuming the conductance of resting sodium is not changed?
    A. −72 mV
    B. −74 mV
    C. −80 mV
    D. −88 mV
    E. −98 mV

14. A 24-year-old soldier suffers burns on more than 60% of his body surface, resulting in a decrease in serum K^+ from a normal value of 4 mEq/L to 2.5 mEq/L. Which of the following pairs of changes best describes the resting membrane potential and the Nernst potential of K^+ in a cardiac myocyte after injury? Resting membrane potential K Nernst potential + Option 1 Less negative Less negative Option 2 Less negative More negative Option 3 More negative Less negative Option 4 More negative More negative Option 5 No change No change
    A. Option A
    B. Option B
    C. Option C
    D. Option D
    E. Option E

15. In a neuron with a resting membrane potential of minus 65 mV, for which of the following ions the distribution across the neuronal membrane represents the lowest potential electromotive force (EMF)?
    A. Potassium
    B. Chloride
    C. Sodium
    D. Calcium
    E. Phosphate

16. A lecturer asks a medical student during a lecture 'Which of the following best defines the concept of an electrochemical equilibrium potential?'
    A. It is the potential reached when the chemical gradient of an ion across a membrane is zero
    B. It is the potential approached during the hydrolysis of ions across a semi-permeable membrane down their concentration gradients
    C. It is the potential of a cell at rest, when most voltage-gated ion channels are closed
    D. It is the potential measured across a reverse osmosis membrane when there is no net movement of water
    E. It is the potential at which there is no net movement of an ionic species across a membrane to which it is permeable

17. After a hard race, a marathon runner drinks a large amount of a hypotonic drink. What effect could be expected on the extracellular fluid (ECF)?
    A. Decrease in volume and becomes hypertonic with respect to the ICF
    B. Decrease in volume and becomes hypotonic with respect to the ICF
    C. Increase in volume and becomes hypotonic with respect to the ICF
    D. Increase in volume and becomes hypertonic with respect to the ICF
    E. Increase in volume and becomes isotonic with respect to the ICF

18. A 22-year-old male participates in a 10 km race on a at 32 °C day. If he loses 3 L of sweat and also drinks 3 L of water during the race, which of the following changes would you expect, compared to normal, after absorption of the water? Intracellular volume Intracellular osmolarity Extracellular volume Extracellular osmolarity Option 1 ↑ ↑ ↑ ↑ Option 2 ↑ ↓ ↓ ↓ Option 3 ↔ ↓ ↔ ↔ Option 4 ↓ ↑ ↑ ↑ Option 5 ↓ ↓ ↓ ↓
   A. Option 1 **B. Option 2** C. Option 3
   D. Option 4 E. Option 5

19. A 60-year-old patient appears dehydrated, with a hematocrit of 0.55 (55%) and a plasma protein concentration of 8.8 g/100 mL (normal ~7). After obtaining a plasma sample, hyponatremia is verified, with a plasma sodium concentration of 110 mmol/L and a plasma osmolarity of 240 mOsm/L. It is decided to administer 2 L of sodium chloride at 3%. Her body weight was 80 kg before administering the liquid. Assuming that: Volume of intracellular fluid = 40% of body weight before administration of fluid Volume of extracellular fluid = 20% of body weight before administration of fluid Molecular weight of NaCl = 58.5 g/mol No excretion of water or electrolytesCalculate approximate osmolarity in plasma after administration of NaCl solution and before reaching osmotic equilibrium.
   A. 240 mOsm/L B. 251 mOsm/L
   C. 265 mOsm/L **D. 286 mOsm/L**
   E. 327 mOsm/L

20. The molarity of a 2% NaCl solution is 340 mmol/L. The molecular weight of NaCl is 58.5. What is the osmolarity of a 2% NaCl solution (in mOsm/L)?
   A. 170 B. 340 C. 510
   D. 680 E. 420

21. Human and rabbit erythrocytes are in equilibrium in different isotonic saline solutions (300 mOsm/L NaCl). Human erythrocytes are then introduced into a 300 mOsm/L glycerol solution, which causes them to swell and burst. However, the rabbit erythrocytes introduced in 300 mOsm/L glycerol do not swell or explode. From this information, which of the following conclusions is true about the 300 mOsm/L glycerol solution in the different cell types? Human erythrocytes Rabbit erythrocytes Option 1 Hypertonic and hyperosmotic Hypotonic and hypoosmotic Option 2 Hypotonic and hypoosmotic Hypertonic and hyperosmotic Option 3 Hypotonic and isosmotic Isotonic and isosmotic Option 4 Isotonic and hypoosmotic Isotonic and hyperosmotic Option 5 Isotonic and isosmotic Hypotonic and isosmotic Option 6 Isotonic and hyperosmotic Isotonic and isosmotic
   A. Option 1 B. Option 2
   C. Option 3 D. Option 4
   E. Option 5 F. Option 6

VIVA / SHORT QUESTION

'All topics of General Physiology and Body Fluids

1. Define homeostasis.
   Ans: Homeostasis is defined as the maintenance of constancy of the internal environment of the body.

2. Who introduced the concept of *milieu intérieur?*
   Ans: Claude Bernard

3. Who coined the term homeostasis?
   Ans: Walter Cannon

4. What is a negative feedback system?
   Ans: When there is a change in the level of the variable, the negative feedback system brings the variable back to the normal range of the set point.

5. What are the components of the negative feedback system?
   Ans:
   i) A sensor that detects the change in variable,
   ii) A control center that receives input from the sensor and initiates command signal, and
   iii) An effector that brings in responses to bring the variable back to the normal range of the set point.

6. Give examples of negative feedback system.
   Ans: Body temperature regulation, Blood pressure regulation, Regulation of secretion of thyroxine, cortisol, etc.

7. What is 'gain' of a feedback control system?
   Ans: Gain is the magnitude of efficiency with which homeostatic control system maintains a balanced condition. Bigger the gain, more robust is the system.

8. What is a positive feedback system?
   Ans: In a positive feedback system, increase in the variable triggers processes that further increase the variable.

9. Give examples of positive feedback system.(for details see page 9-10, 4th Edn)
   Ans: Parturition reflex initiated by oxytocin, LH surge, The Hodgkin's cycle, Activation of digestive enzymes, Enzyme cascade hypothesis of coagulation

10. What is the role of kidney in homeostasis?
    Ans: The kidneys regualate homeostasis of many physiological variables such as regulation of blood volume and blood pressure, pH balance, electrolyte composition of body fluids, and osmolarity of fluid compartments.

11. What is the role of sympathovagal balance in homeostasis?
    Ans: As sympathetic and vagal stimulation to the organs have opposite influences, a balance between them (sympathovagal balance) is essential for smooth conduct of cardio-respiratory, endocrinal and other visceral and metabolic functions.

12. What is intracellular homeostasis?
    Ans: Maintenance of the of intracellular fluid volume and composition

13. What is the Fluid Mosaic Model of cell membrane?
    Ans: Cell membrane consists of a double-layer of phospholipid that contains protein molecules. The membrane lipids (Phospholipids, Glycolipids, Cholesterol) are present in the fluid form that allows the *flexibility of the membrane.*

14. What is the function of the lipid bilayer?
    Ans: Lipid bilayer makes the membrane semipermeable. *Lipid soluble substances* like oxygen and alcohol can pass easily through the cell membrane. *Water soluble substances* like urea and glucose cannot pass easily.

15. What are the functions of cell membrane?
    Ans: It maintains a constant and distinctive intracellular environment, maintains cell volume, maintains a potential difference across the membrane in neurons and muscle cells and helps in recognizing foreign cells or antigens.

16. What are the functions of mitochondria?
    Ans: Cellular oxidation of nutrients such as glucose, Formation of ATP via TCA cycle that generates 36 ATP molecules

17. What are the functions of rough endoplasmic reticulum?
    Ans: Protein synthesis and glycosylation

18. What are the functions of smooth endoplasmic reticulum?
    Ans: i) Synthesis of lipids
    ii) Storage of calcium ions in muscle, called sarcoplasmic reticulum
    iii) Part of intracellular transport system
    iv) Site for the detoxification or neutralization of hormones and toxic substances

19. What are the functions of lysosomes?
    Ans:
    i) Digestive organelle
    ii) Bactericidal (have Lysozymes)
    iii) Fertilization of ovum
    iv) Autolysis
    v) Remove intracellular products of metabolism from the cell

20. What are the functions of Golgi apparatus?
    Ans:
    i) Formation of secretary vesicles, glycoproteins, primary lysosomes
    ii) Transport of materials to other organelles and cell surface
    iii) What are the functions of Golgi apparatus?

21. What are the functions of peroxisomes?
Ans: Subcellular respiratory organelles, contain oxidases that promote oxidation of lipids

22. What are Microfilaments and their functions?
Ans: Microfilaments are long solid filaments made up of actin. They are major contractile fibers of the cell and help in:
i) Change in cell shape and cell movement.
ii) Phagocytosis, transport and secretion of cellular materials, cell contraction, cell discharge, movement of secretory granules (e.g. release of granules from platelets)
iii) Movement of chromosome and cell division
iv) As anchoring proteins
v) Microvilli movement
vi) Cell movement on a surface (Microfilaments in the lamellopodia)
vii) Form focal adhesion complexes (FAC) by interacting with integrin receptors
viii) Microfilaments are also used by some molecular motors as tracks

23. What are the Microtubules and their functions?
Ans: Microtubules are long hollow tubular structures made up of α-tubulin and β-tubulin, show the property of re-aggregating (assembly) at the +ve end and disaggregating (disassembly) at the –ve end. Microtubules:
i) Help in transport of vesicles and organelles from one part of the cell to another.
ii) Contribute to the maintenance of cell strength and cell shape.
iii) Help in the formation of spindles that move chromosomes during mitotic cell division.
iv) Are the pillars for structure and function of cilia.
v) Contribute to cell motility.

24. What are the functions Intermediate filaments?
Ans: They connect the nuclear membrane to the cell membrane and also membranes of cell organelles, Resist rupture of cell from external pressure, Cell markers

25. What are the Molecular motors and their functions?
Ans: Microtubulebased molecular motors (Kinesin and Dynein) and Actinbased molecular motors (Myosin)
i) Kinesin and cytoplasmic Dynein make movement of molecules along the microtubules, axonemal Dynein cause beating of cilia and flagella.
ii) Myosin cause muscle contraction, contraction of intestinal villi, cell migration

26. Classify intercellular junctions.
A. Junctions that tie cells together
  1. Tight junctions
  2. Anchoring junctions
    a. Cell to cell (Desmosome, Zonula adherens)
    b. Cell to basal lamina (Hemidesmosome, Focal adhesion)
B. Junctions that allow transfer of ions and small molecules
  1. Gap junctions

27. What are the functions Tight junctions?
Ans: They form:
i) Selective permeability barrier that prevent transport of macromolecules from the luminal fluid into the interstitial space
ii) Paracellular transport of solutes and solvents. (e.g. through the leaky channels, small size water soluble particles pass through tight junctions)
iii) Blood-brain barrier (tight junctions between endothelial cells of cerebral blood vessels)
iv) Blood-aqueous barrier (in the ciliary bodies, between the cells of inner nonpigmented epithelium)

28. What are the Anchoring junctions?
Ans: i) Desmosomes are *focal thickening* of two adjacent cell membranes separated by a gap of 25 nm. The intercellular space between the two membrane thickenings contains filamentous cell adhesion materials such as desmogleins and cadherins
ii) Zonula adherens is located below the base of tight junctions, it is the *major site of attachment for intracellular microfilaments*, .
iii) Hemidesmosome contain integrins. Microfilaments are attached to it intracellularly.
iv) Focal adhesions (focal spots) connect cell to the basal lamina. Intracellularly, they are associated with actin filaments and assist in cell movement.

29. What are the cell adhesion molecules and their functions?
Ans: Cells are attached to each other and to the basal lamina by cell adhesion molecules. They are Integrins, IgG superfamily proteins, cadherins and selectins. They
i) Zip cell to cell
ii) Cause cell movement.
iii) Transmission of signals into and out of the cell
iv) Help in inflammation and wound healing
v) Prevent apoptosis

30. What is apoptosis? Give example and mention its importance.
Ans: Apoptosis is the programmed cell death.
Examples are:
i) Death of neurons in central nervous system during brain development and synapse formation
ii) Degeneration of many tissues like web in the fingers during fetal development
iii) Apoptosis of eosinophils
Importance: Decreased apoptosis - cancer and autoimmune diseases
Increased apoptosis - Alzheimer's disease, Parkinson's disease

Transport across the Cell Membrane and Membrane Potential

1. Classify transport processes.
A. Passive transports
  1. Simple diffusion
  2. Facilitated diffusion
  3. Osmosis
  4. Filtration
  5. Bulk flow
  6. Solvent drag

B. Active transports
   1. Primary active transport
   2. Secondary active transport

C. Vesicular transports
   1. Exocytosis
   2. Endocytosis

D. Transport across epithelia
   1. Transcellular transport
   2. Paracellular transport

31. What are the types of carrier proteins?

Ans: Three types: uniport, symport and antiport

i) Uniport: Transports one substance across the membrane. For e.g., Na^+ channels transport Na^+ and K^+ channels transport K^+.

ii) Symport (Co-transport): Transports two or more substances across the membrane *in the same direction*. For e.g. Transport of Na^+ and glucose in the intestine or kidney tubule

iii) Antiport (Counter-transport): Transports substances *in opposite directions* in which one substance is transported into the cell and other substance to the outside. For e.g. sodium-potassium pump (Na^+-K^+ ATPase) transports 3 Na^+ out of the cell, and 2 K^+ into the cell; Na^+-H^+ exchanger transports Na^+ inward and H^+outward.

32. Differences between active and passive transport processes.

Ans:

	Active transport	**Passive transport**
1. Nature of transport	Against electrochemical gradient	Along the gradient
2. Utilization of energy	ATP hydrolysis occurs	Not needed
3. Saturation kinetics	Present	May not be present

33. What are the factors that determine the rate of diffusion across the cell membrane?

Ans: Determined by (a) Properties of the substance and (b) Properties of the membrane.

(a) Factors determining properties of the substance:

i) Concentration and electrical gradients of the substance

ii) Permeability of the substance through the membrane. It is affected by:

Lipid-solubility: Permeability is *proportional to their lipid solubility* of the substance.

- Molecular size: Permeability is inversely proportional to the molecular size (the effective molecular size of the hydrated K+ is greater than that of Na+)

- Charge on the molecule: As the cell membrane has negative interior, cations easily enter from outside into the cell and anions in the opposite direction.

- Temperature: Rate of diffusion is high at higher body temperature

- Distribution of channels in the membrane: Higher the number of channels, greater is the rate of diffusion

- **Pressure gradient:** Diffusion is more from high pressure to low pressure

(b) Factors determining properties of the membrane:

i) Cross sectional area of the membrane: Rate of diffusion is directly proportional to the surface area Bigger area shows higher diffusion

ii) Thickness of the membrane: Rate of diffusion is inversely proportional to the thickness of the membrane More thickness shows less diffusion

34. What is facilitated diffusion or carrier-mediated diffusion?

Ans: When diffusion is facilitated by a carrier protein in the membrane.

35. What are the features of facilitated diffusion?

Ans:

i) *Faster rate of transport* (transport of hydrophilic molecules occurs at a faster rate)

ii) *Saturation kinetics* (when all the available binding sites on the carrier proteins are occupied, the transport system is saturated)

iii) *Competitive inhibition* (Many substances *share same carrier protein*, they compete to bind with the carrier protein. Thus, one substance decreases the transport of the other. For e.g., transport of D-glucose slows down in presence of D-galactose.

iv) *Specificity* (The carrier proteins are specific for different molecules, for e.g. the carrier protein for protein does not transport cholesterol or fatty acid)

36. What are the differences between simple diffusion and facilitated diffusion?

	Simple diffusion	Facilitated diffusion
1. Mode of diffusion	No carrier molecule	Carrier molecule involved
2. Saturation kinetics	No saturation kinetics	Has saturation kinetics
3. Competitive inhibition	Absent	Present
4. Rate of diffusion	May be slow	Faster
5. Specificity	No specificity	Carrier protein may be specific

37. What is Osmosis?

Ans: Osmosis is the transport of solvent from the solution with the lower concentration of solutes to the solution with higher concentration of solute, when both the solutions are separated by a semipermeable membrane.

38. What is osmotic effectiveness of a substance? Give examples.

Ans: Ability of a substance to maintain a stable osmotic pressure. The substance should be confined to one side of the membrane.

Osmotically effective: Plasma protein, Sodium chloride

Osmotically ineffective: Urea

39. What is Osmotic Pressure?

Ans: It is the hydrostatic pressure necessary to prevent osmotic flow of water.

40. What is Oncotic Pressure?

Ans: The osmotic pressure of plasma is known as *oncotic pressure*, which is *25 mmHg*

41. What is Osmolality and Osmolarity?

Ans: Osmolality of a solution refers to the number of osmoles (number of osmotically active particles) dissolved in a kilogram of water. Osmolarity refers to the number of osmoles in one liter of plasma.

42. Define active transport, give examples and mention types.

Ans: The transport process that utilizes energy and occurs against the gradient.

Examples: Na^+–K^+ ATPase, H^+–K^+ ATPase

Types: i) Primary active transport ii) Secondary active transport

43. What are the functions of Na^+–K^+ ATPase?

Ans:

i) Cytosolic ion concentration: It pumps three Na^+ ions out of the cell and two K^+ into the cell, thus it maintains high concentration of K^+ and low concentration of Na^+ in the cell.
ii) Cell volume: By maintaining ion concentration on both sides of the cell, it regulates water movement across the cell membrane and maintains cell volume, thus prevents swelling and rupture.
iii) Protein synthesis: High intracellular concentration of K^+ is essential for protein synthesis.
iv) Resting membrane potential: It contributes - 4 mV to the genesis of RMP by creating a net negative potential inside the membrane as it pumps three positive charges out and two positive charges in.
v) Hormone actions: It mediates action of many hormones e.g. thyroxine, aldosterone and insulin.

44. Define secondary active transport and give examples.

Ans: The transfer one solute against its concentration gradient by using the energy generated by gradient of another solute.

Example: Reabsorption of glucose from the kidney tubule or intestine

The Na^+-K^+ pump decreases concentration gradient of Na^+inside the cell, this causes facilitated diffusion of Na^+ from the lumen into the cells by the carrier protein (sodium-glucose cotransporter), which also transports glucose in the same direction.

45. What is vesicular transport?

Ans: Formation and transport of vesicles are facilitated by some vesicular transport proteins, such as clathrin, coating proteins, dynamin and docking proteins.

46. What are the types of vesicular transport?

Ans: Three types: endocytosis, exocytosis and transcytosis

i) Endocytosis is the process of transport in which a substance is *taken into the cell by means of vesicle formation.* It is of three types: phagocytosis, receptor-mediated endocytosis and pinocytosis
ii) Exocytosis is the process of export from the cell. Hormones, neurotransmitters, digestive enzymes and undigested foreign particles are released form cells by exocytosis
iii) Transcytosis is the process when vesicular transport is limited within the cell, also called cytopemisis.

47. What is Donnan effect?

Ans: Presence of nondiffusible ion on one side of the membrane affects the distribution of other ions to which membrane is permeable. This results in asymmetrical distribution of total ions across the cell membrane.

48. What is resting membrane potential (RMP)?

Ans: RMP is the electrical potential difference existing just across the plasma membrane of a resting cell. In neurons, the RMP is –70 mV.

49. What are the factors contributing to the genesis of resting membrane potential (RMP)?

Ans:

i) Permeability of the membrane to K^+: At rest, permeability of the membrane to K^+ is higher. As K^+ is more inside the cell, it easily diffuses out of the cell that creates negativity inside the cell.
ii) Relative impermeability of the membrane of resting cells to Na^+: At rest, membrane is less permeable to Na^+ than to K^+. Therefore, K^+ exit is not balanced by Na^+ entry (more K^+ goes out). Hence, interior of the cell remains relatively negative.
iii) Permeability to anions: Exit of K^+ (the cation) is not accompanied by exit of same amount of anions as permeability of anions at rest is also not same as that of K^+. Therefore, more negative ion remains inside.
iv) Role of Na^+-K^+ pump: It pumps out three Na^+ for two K^+ to come in, thus a relative negativity is created inside.

50. What is the distribution of body fluid in extracellular fluid (ECF) and intracellular fluid (ICF) volume?

Ans: Total body water is 60% of body weight, ICF is 20% and ECF is 40% of body weight.

In a 70 kg man, TBW is 42L, ICF is 28L and ECF is 14L.

ICF is 2/3rd and ECF is 1/3rd of total body water.

51. How is the body fluid volume measured?

Ans: The volume of fluid compartment is measured by the *indicator dilution principle*; V= A/C, where, V is the volume of the fluid compartment, A is the amount of a substance injected into the fluid compartment, and C is the final concentration attained.

52. What are the characteristics of an ideal indicator?
Ans: The indicator should:
i) be relatively easy to measure
ii) remain in the compartment being measured.
iii) not change the fluid distribution in the compartment being measured.
iv) be non-toxic.
v) mix evenly throughout the compartment being measured.
vi) remain unchanged by the body during the mixing period or the amount changed must be known.

53. How do you calculate ECF volume?
Ans: Radioactive inulin, Cl^- ($^{36}Cl^-$ and $^{38}Cl^-$), ^{82}Br, mannitol, sucrose, sulphate, thiosulphate, thiocyanate and ferrocyanide.

54. How do you calculate plasma volume?
Ans: Plasma is 5% of body weight; In a 70 kg man, Plasma is 3.5L
Plasma is 25% of the ECF; when ECF is 14 L, Plasma is 3.5L
Volume of plasma can be calculated from blood volume and red cell volume (Hematocrit) as:

$$\text{Plasma volume} = \text{Blood volume} \times \frac{100 - \text{Hematocrit}}{100}$$

Also, measured by Evans Blue Dye, Radio-iodinated albumin/gamma globulin/ fibrinogen

55. How do you calculate total body water?
Ans: Deuterium oxide (D2O, heavy water), Tritium oxide and aminopyrine

56. How do you calculate red cell volume?
Ans: Red cell volume = Total blood volume - Plasma volume
It is also calculated by injecting red cells tagged with radioactive isotopes ^{51}Cr, ^{59}Fe or ^{32}P.

57. Why dehydration is common and rapid in children?
Ans: The total volume of ECF is much smaller in children than in adults. Also, the regulatory mechanisms for maintaining ECF volume are not well developed in infants and children. Therefore, dehydration is more common and occurs rapidly in them.

58. What is interstitial fluid volume and how do you calculate it?
Ans: It is the fluid present in the space between the cells.
It is calculated as ECF – Plasma = 14L - 3.5 L= 10.5 L

59. What is edema?
Ans: Accumulation of *excess free fluid in interstitial tissue space* is called edema. Edema can be due to increased filtration of fluid into interstitial space as occurs in heart failure or decreased removal fluid from interstitial space as occurs in lymphatic obstruction.

60. What are the concentrations of Na^+, K^+, Cl^-. HCO_3^- in ECF and ICF?

Ions (mmol/L of H^2O)	ECF	ICF
Na^+	145	12
K^+	5	140
Cl^-	110	5
HCO_3^-	27	10

61. What is transcellular fluid?
Ans: Fluid present in another compartment of the body is called transcellular fluid. It includes fluid in the secretion of exocrine digestive glands, cerebrospinal fluid, pleural, peritoneal, synovial and pericardial fluids, intraocular (aqueous and vitreous humors) fluids, bile, luminal fluids of the gut and fluid in the cochlea and kidney tubules. It is 1.5% of body weight (1-2 L).

62. What is blood? Give its composition.
Ans: Blood is defined as liquid connective tissue that fills the heart and blood vessels.
It is composed of cellular components (45%) and plasma (55%). The cells are red blood cells (erythrocytes), white blood cells (leucocytes), and platelets. The normal blood volume in an average adult is 5–6 liters, which accounts for about 8% of the body weight.

SECTION II - BLOOD

MULTIPLE CHOICE QUESTIONS

1. A 55-year-old male has a 32-year history of alcoholism and liver disease. He goes to the doctor suffering from swelling of legs and feet. In which of the following factors would a decrease be the most likely cause of edema?
   A. Arteriolar dilation
   B. Hydrostatic capillary pressure|
   C. Filtration coefficient|
   D. Capillary colloid osmotic pressure
   E. Osmotic pressure of the interstitial liquid|F. Plasma colloid osmotic pressure

2. A 77-year-old man has a 33-year history of alcoholism and liver disease. He goes to his doctor for swelling of both legs. In which of the following factors would a decrease be likely to contribute to the development of leg edema?
   A. Hydrostatic capillary pressure
   B. Femoral venous pressure
   C. Blood pressure
   D. Liver lymphatic flow
   E. Plasma albumin concentration

3. In a normal healthy person, which of the following blood components has the longest lifespan?
   A. Macrophages
   B. T cells
   C. Erythrocytes
   D. Platelets
   E. Neutrophils

4. Blood is made up of the formed elements (erythrocytes, leukocytes and platelets) and plasma. Plasma consists of 90% water, 9% organic compounds (proteins, amino acids and hormones) and 1% organic salts. Thus, when 0.9% normal saline is administered in the emergency department, what components of those listed above are not present in the intravenous solution?
   A. Organic plasma compounds and formed elements of blood
   B. Organic plasma compounds and organic plasma salts|C. Organic plasma salts and the formed elements of blood|D. Organic compounds in plasma and water|E. Water and the formed elements of blood

5. Which of the following is a cytokine which is a growth factor for pluripotent stem cells?
   A. Tumour necrosis factor α
   B. Granulocyte–monocyte colony-stimulating factor (GCSF)
   C. Interleukin 3
   D. Interleukin 4
   E. Interleukin 5

6. In adults, red blood cells are produced in bone (liver in fetus). Where are red cells produced in bones?
   A. Yellow marrow   B. Periosteum
   C. Haversian canal system   **D. Red marrow**
   E. Volkmann's canals

7. Haemoglobin plays an important role in carrying oxygen in the red blood cells. Which of the following statements about the reaction of haemoglobin and oxygen is true?
   A. Haemoglobin increases the oxygen-carrying capacity of the blood by about twofold
   B. The globin molecules bind to the oxygen molecules|
   C. Each haemoglobin molecule is capable of binding up to four oxygen molecules
   D. Binding of the haemoglobin with the first oxygen molecule reduces the affinity for binding to a second oxygen molecule|E. Binding to an oxygen molecule increases the likelihood of the haem moieties assuming a tense (T) state

8. In patients with chronic obstructive pulmonary disease, the packed cell volume (PCV; i.e. haematocrit) is often raised. What does the haematocrit measure?
   A. The ratio of the volume of red blood cells to the volume of whole blood
   B. The size of red blood cells
   C. The risk of blood clot formation
   D. The percentage of haemoglobin saturated with oxygen
   E. The fraction of plasma capable of carrying oxygen

9. Red cells are biconcave disc-shaped cells lacking a nucleus, since this is extruded while the cell is maturing in the bone marrow. What is the life span of red cells?
   A. 28 days   B. 6 months   C. 4 days
   D. 120 days   E. 14 days

10. Viscosity is a measure of the internal friction within a fluid. In plasma, the presence of plasma proteins makes its viscosity slightly greater than that of water; however, the viscosity of whole blood (relative viscosity) is about four times that of water, an important factor for blood flow. Blood viscosity is mainly determined by the haematocrit, which is normally about 0.42–0.53 in men and 0.36–0.45 in women. What is the characteristic feature of haematocrit?
    A. High fibrinogen levels
    B. Increase in the number of red cells
    C. Low viscosity levels, leading to reduced perfusion
    D. Reduced apparent viscosity of blood, leading to high levels of shear
    E. Volume of packed red cells per unit volume of blood

11. DNA synthesis is impaired in megaloblastic anaemias. The metabolic pathway for DNA replication involves both vitamins B12 (cobalamin, Cbl) and folate. In which of the following organs is cobalamin released from dietary proteins?
   A. stomach B. duodenum C. jejunum
   D. ileum E. liver

12. A healthy 3-year-old girl is taken to the emergency department because she has an undetectable nosebleed. She has a history of ear infections that have improved after treatment. Her temperature is high. She has numerous small bruises on her arms and legs. The analysis is as follows: Hemoglobin 4.6 g/dL Leukocyte count 3,000/mm3 Reticulocyte count 0.1% Platelet count 12,000/mm3 Which of the following factors provides the most likely explanation for these results?
   A. Anemia due to loss of blood
   B. Aplastic anemia
   C. Sickle cell disease
   D. Infectious Mononucleosis
   E. Folate deficiency anemia

13. What is the safest and most cost-effective treatment for patients with polycythemia vera?
   A. High altitudes
   B. Decrease in iron concentration
   C. Therapeutic phlebotomy
   D. Decrease in erythropoietin concentration
   E. Erythropoietin injection

14. A 67-year-old man attends his GP for a well man check. He reports his health has been good though recently he has noticed some intermittent constipation which is relieved by laxatives and he finds he can't walk for as long as he used too. The GP organizes some blood tests which show a haemoglobin of 80 g/L (normal range 130–160) and an MCV of 60 fL (normal range 78–101). The haematologist comments that the cells are hypochromic. Which vitamin or mineral deficiency is the most likely cause of this presentation?
   A. Vitamin K
   B. Nicotinic acid
   C. Folate
   D. Iron
   E. Nicotinic acid

15. A 45-year-old woman has been complaining of tiredness and attends her GP. He does a full blood count which shows a haemoglobin of 100 g/L (normal range 120–150) and an MCV of 105 fL (normal range 78–101). Her B12 levels are normal and a bone marrow aspirate is organized which shows megaloblastic changes.Which vitamin/ mineral deficiency is the most likely cause of this presentation?
   A. Vitamin K
   B. Vitamin C
   C. Folate
   D. Nicotinic acid E. Iron

16. A mother with B+ blood who has always been healthy has just given birth to her second child. She had been given blood transfusion (O positive) an year before, The father is of blood of group O-. Knowing that the child is of group O- (O, Rh-), what would you expect to find in this child?
   A. The child will suffer from erythroblastosis fetalis due to rhesus incompatibility
   B. The child will suffer from erythroblastosis fetalis due to ABO blood group incompatibility
   C. The child's antibodies will be transferred to the mother
   D. The child has no chance of developing hemolytic disease of the newborn
   E. The son will suffer from hepatosplenomegaly

17. Erythroblastosis fetalis due to Rhesus incompatibility may result in the newborn suffering from all of the following conditions, EXCEPT:
   A. Severe anemia B. kernicterus
   C. Hemolysis **D. Atrophy of the spleen and liver**
   E. Hepatosplenomegaly

18. Which of the following couples cannot be the biological parents of a child with AB blood type?
   A. Mother AB, father AB **B. Mother AB, father OO**
   C. Mother OB, father OA D. Mother OA, father BB
   E. Mother AA, father OB

19. A pregnant woman comes to your office. She's AB Rh+ and her husband is A Rh-. This is their second child. What must be done on this occasion?
   A. Nothing
   B. She should be administered anti-D immunoglobulin at that time
   C. The child should be administered anti-D immunoglobulin after birth
   D. Anti-D immunoglobulin should be administered to the child if the baby is Rh+
   E. The child should be administered anti-D through the placenta

20. A previously healthy 22-year-old A+ woman is admitted to the hospital for a digestive hemorrhage. Her hematocrit level is 25%. She receives three units of blood. During the administration of the fourth unit, she develops severe low back pain, dyspnea, fever, a drop in blood pressure and red-brown urine. Which of the following is the most likely cause of her anemia?
   A. ABO incompatibility
   B. Bacterial contamination of blood
   C. Rh incompatibility
   D. Elevated immunoglobulin E (IgE) levels
   E. Viral contamination of blood

21. A 45-year-old male with O blood type receives chemotherapy and, as a result, his platelet count drops, so he needs a transfusion. Which of the following blood groups would be suitable for platelet donors?
   A. Type AB only **B. Type O only**
   C. Types A, B, AB and O D. Types A and B only
   E. Types A, B and AB only

22. A 16-year-old boy is involved in a traffic accident and suffers a serious injury with internal bleeding requiring a blood transfusion. His blood is typed and it is seen to be AB Rh negative. What type of blood can he receive?
    A. Any blood type
    B. A−, B−, AB− or O−
    C. A−, B− or AB+
    D. Only A− or B−
    E. Only A−

23. Neutrophils are the commonest white cell found in peripheral blood (50–70% total white cells) with a lifespan of around 8–10 h.How many lobes are contained in a neutrophil nucleus?
    A. One
    B. Two to five
    C. >10
    D. None
    E. Eight

24. A 20-year-old male goes to the emergency department with a two-week history of diarrhea after a trip abroad. He's admitted to the hospital for dehydration and allergy. Stool sample is positive for ova and parasites. What type of leukocytes would be found in high numbers?
    A. Eosinophils
    B. Neutrophils
    C. T cells
    D. B cells
    E. Monocytes

25. Giemsa and Wright stains are Romanovsky-type stains (using a combination of dyes derived from eosin and methylene blue). They are used to visualize blood cells. These stains are preferable to hematoxylin and eosin because they clearly show the specific (secondary) granules present in some leukocytes. Since all leukocytes have primary (azurophilic) granules, the presence or absence of secondary granules in Wright/Giemsa staining is the basis for the classical distinction of leukocytes between granulocytes and agranulocytes. What two cell types make up the agranulocyte group?
    A. Neutrophils and basophils
    B. Eosinophils and megakaryocytes
    C. Monocytes and lymphocytes
    D. Erythrocytes and platelets|E. Plasma cells and metamyelocytes

26. Granulocytes are subdivided according to the Romanovsky-type staining pattern for their secondary granules. In basophils, the secondary granules fix the basic methylene blue dye, and they stain dark blue. In eosinophils, the granules fix the acid dye eosin, appearing salmon pink or light pink. Which of the following substances found in the secondary granules of eosinophils, is primarily responsible for the intense red staining of the cell and produces a strong cytotoxic effect on protozoa and helminths?
    A. Myeloperoxidase
    B. Immunoglobulin A
    C. Major basic protein
    D. Lysozyme
    E. Heparin sulfate

27. 2.Which of the following statements about negative selection during lymphocytic development is more accurate?
    A. The mechanism of negative selection is the death of cells whose antigen receptors are not stimulated by their own antigens.
    B. The mechanism of negative selection is actively induced apoptosis by the recognition of own antigens by the receptor for the antigen.
    C. Negative selection ensures that there is a repertoire of T lymphocytes restricted by the MHC itself.
    D. Negative selection occurs only at the maturation of the T-lymphocyte and not at the maturation of the B-lymphocyte.
    E. The main mechanism of negative selection is inhibition of the expression of the receptor for the antigen.

28. Which of the following is NOT an example of a control point in lymphocyte maturation that contributes to the selective maturation of cells with useful antigen receptors?
    A. B-lymphocyte precursors that cannot express heavy Ig γ chains die from apoptosis.
    B. Precursors of T lymphocytes that cannot express TCR β chains die by apoptosis.
    C. Immature B lymphocytes that bind to an antigen of their own with a high affinity die from apoptosis.
    D. Developing T lymphocytes that do not express TCR α chains die by apoptosis.
    E. Developing T-lymphocytes that recognize molecules of their own major histocompatibility complex (MHC) with high affinity die from apoptosis.

29. A 12-month-old child with frequent pyogenic infections and three episodes of pneumonia requiring admission turns out to have Bruton's agammaglobulinemia. Treatment is commenced with immunoglobulins, which is an example of:
    A. Active immunization
    B. Passive immunization
    C. Immunosuppression
    D. Desensitization
    E. Quimioprofilaxis

30. Indicate which intracellular molecules that transmit signals and transcription factors are activated by IL-12:
    A. CD40L
    B. CD40
    C. STAT6
    D. STAT4
    E. IL-5

31. Which of the following is NOT a necessary step in the maturation of T and B lymphocytes?
    A. Proliferative expansion of precursor cells
    B. Expression on the cell surface of receptor complexes for the complete antigen
    C. Positive selection
    D. Activation of precursors by foreign antigens
    E. Expression of prereceptor for the antigen

32. Endothelial cells line all blood vessels and these play a central role in preventing unwanted thrombosis.The endothelium provides an effective barrier between the thrombogenic subendothelial cells and

the blood coagulation factors. What is the function of thrombomodulin?
A. Encourages platelet aggregation
B. Activates thrombin
C. Binds to thrombin and inactivates its coagulant activity
D. Potent inhibitor of platelet aggregation
E. Released from the activated platelet and causes vasoconstriction

33. In allergic people, the reaction to certain antigens is manifested as vasodilatation and increased capillary permeability. Which of the following factors is the origin of this allergic reaction?
A. T cells activated in the smooth muscle cells
B. IgA in basophils and mast cells
C. IgA in neutrophils and eosinophils
D. IgE in basophils and mast cells
E. IgE in neutrophils and eosinophils

34. Coagulation disorders may be inherited or acquired, and are the result of deficient or defective functioning of coagulation factors. What is Bernard–Soulier syndrome?
A. Abnormality in platelet Gp IIb-IIIa interaction preventing platelet aggregation
B. Autosomal dominant inherited disorder (although some forms are recessive) associated with a deficiency in circulating von Willebrand factor (vWF)
C. Autosomal recessive inherited disorder where there is reduced complex of Gp1b, factor IX, and factor V which serves as a receptor for vWF leading to lack of platelet plug formation
D. Inherited X-linked disorder where mutations within the factor VIII gene lead to defective function of the factor VIII-C molecule in the coagulation cascade|E. Inherited X-linked disorder where mutations within the factor IX gene lead to defective function of the factor IX molecule in the coagulation cascade

35. A 9-year-old boy is brought to the GP by his mother, who is concerned because of his recurrent nose bleeds. He would also have bleeding from his gums and bruises easily. His maternal uncle died from a gastrointestinal bleed in his 40s.caution had to taken while giving NSAIDs. Blood tests show reduced factor VIII activity:antigen ratio. Which X-linked recessive disorder from the list below is the most likely cause of his presentation?
A. Vitamin D-resistant rickets
B. Fabry disease
C. Lesch–Nyhan syndrome
D. Haemophilia A
E. Duchenne muscular dystrophy

36. A patient comes with a platelet count of 212,000/μL and a bleeding time of 12 min. These results indicate:
A. A decrease in platelet production
B. A defective platelet function
C. An increase in platelet production
D. An increase in platelet destruction
E. A lower-than-normal platelet count

37. A 2-year-old child suffers from easy bruising and has a history of nosebleeds. Physical examination shows several small bruises on the legs. In which of the following clotting factors should a deficiency be suspected for this patient?
A. Prothrombin activator
B. Factor II
C. Factor VIII
D. Factor X
E. Factor V

38. A 6-year-old boy attends the paediatric Emergency Department. His parents have noticed dark urine in the morning. Laboratory investigations reveal intravascular haemolysis. Furthermore, his red blood cells are susceptible to complement-mediated lysis. The patient is most likely suffering from:
A. Sickle cell anaemia
B. Autoimmune haemolytic anaemia
C. Factor V Leiden deficiency
D. Hereditary spherocytosis
E. Paroxysmal nocturnal haemoglobinuria

39. A 65-year-old male with hematemesis and melena has a crescent-shaped duodenal ulcer. Washing removes the clot and shows a blood vessel that was successfully removed by cauterization with a bipolar gold probe. Which of the following is a diagnosis of a duodenal ulcer? Endoscopy Plasma gastrin concentrations Acid secretion rate A No No No B Yes No No C Yes No Yes D Yes Yes No E Yes Yes Yes
A. Option A
B. Option B
C. Option C
D. Option D
E. Option E

40. 7.A newborn baby of 2-months-old is unable to produce antibodies because of immature immune system, but resistant to infection and shows antibodies in blood, and intestinal mucosa. Which of the following are the most likely antibodies found in the newborn?
A. IgG
B. IgA
C. IgM & IgA
D. IgG & IgM
E. IgG & IgA

VIVA / SHORT QUESTION

1. What are the functions of blood?

   Ans:
   1) Respiratory functions: transports oxygen from lungs to tissues, and carbon dioxide from tissues to the lungs.
   2) Transport medium: for various hormones, chemical substances, nutrients, vitamins, etc.
   3) Temperature regulation: conducts heat from the interior of body to the surface through blood vessels.
   4) Excretory function: helps in excretion of waste materials by transporting them from different parts of the body to the kidney.
   5) Water homeostasis: 55% of blood contains plasma and 92% of plasma contains water.
   6) Acid-base balance: The protein and Hb buffers play important role in maintaining acid base balance of the body. Also, bicarbonate in blood buffers the acids.
   7) Immunity: Blood contains T lymphocytes and immunonoglobulins that play major role in cellular and humoral immunity respectively.
   8) Storage: Blood is the storage site of electrolytes, nutrients, chemicals, hormones, etc.
   9) Body color: Blood provides natural color to the body. In anemia and hypovolemia, body becomes pale.
   10) Nutritive functions: Blood delivers all nutrients such as glucose, lipids, proteins, vitamins, minerals, etc to all tissues of the body for their utilization and storage.
   11) Oncotic pressure: The albumin present in blood exerts osmotic pressure, known as oncotic pressure that controls capillary filtration and prevents edema formation.

2. What is buffy coat?

   Ans: The thin middle layer that separates the upper plasma and lower red cell mass after centrifugation of blood is the buffy coat. It contains leucocytes and platelets.

   In diseases, abnormal cells are found in the buffy coat like *LE cells* in systemic lupus erythematosus and atypical or *primitive blood cells* (atypical mononuclear cells, promyelocytes, metamyelocytes, blast cells, megakaryocytes etc.) in malignant or premalignant conditions.

3. What is effective blood volume?

   Ans: The blood volume present in the circulation that actually helps in perfusion of tissue.

   Effective blood volume = Total blood volume – the volume that is sequestrated.

4. Give the composition of plasma.
   1. Water (92%)
   2. Solids or Solutes (8%): plasma proteins make 90% of solids
      a. Inorganic
         i. Anions: Chloride, bicarbonate, phosphates, sulphates, etc.
         ii. Cations: Na^+, K^+, Ca^{++}, Mg^{++} etc.
      b. Organic
         i. Colloids: Plasma proteins
         ii. Crystalloids: Glucose, lipid, urea, uric acid, etc.

5. What is serum?

   Ans: Plasma without clotting factors is called serum. The serum is separated from blood by allowing the blood to coagulate.

6. What are the types of plasma proteins? List their functions.

   Ans: Three types: Albumin (4–5.5 g%), Globulin (1.5–3 g%), and Fibrinogen (0.3 g%).
   1) Osmotic pressure: The osmotic pressure of plasma due to plasma proteins, mainly albumin is called *oncotic pressure*, which is 25 mmHg.
   2) Viscosity: Plasma proteins, mainly fibrinogen contribute to about 50% of the viscosity of blood
   3) Immunity: Gamma globulins mediate humoral immunity
   4) Coagulation: Fibrinogen that forms fibrin thread, the final step in blood coagulation.
   5) Transport: Plasma proteins serve as carrier molecule for transport of various substances like hormones, drugs, metals, etc.
   6) Buffering: Proteins act as buffers to maintain acid-base balance of the body.
   7) Protein store: Plasma proteins serve as *mobile protein reserve* of the body, which can be utilized for tissue growth, especially in situations of protein depletion.
   8) Synthetic function: Plasma proteins provide substrate for the synthesis of protein hormones like erythropoietin, etc. and various enzymes
   9) Determination of ESR: ESR mostly depends on the plasma concentration of fibrinogen.

7. What is hemopoiesis? What are its sites and stages?

   Ans: Hemopoiesis is the process of formation (development, maturation and release) of blood cells. During intrauterine life, hemopoiesis occurs in the yolk sac and later in the liver and spleen, after birth, it occurs in the bone marrow.

   Three stages: Mesoblastic stage (yolk sac); Hepatic stage (liver and spleen); Medullary stage (bone marrow)

8. What are the types of bone marrow and their functions?

   Ans: Two types: Red marrow that produces blood cells; Yellow marrow does not participate in hemopoiesis

9. List some hemopoietic growth factors.

   Ans: Erythropoietin, Interleukin 1,2,3,4,5,6,8, Colony stimulating factors (M-CSF, G-CSF, GM-CSF, CSF-1) Leukemia inhibitory factor (LIF), Stroma cell derived cytokine (SCDC)

Red Blood Cells, Hemoglobins and Blood Indices, Anemia, Polycythemia

10. What is the structure of RBC?

    Ans: It is a circular, non-nucleated and biconcave disc, 7 to 8 μm in diameter

11. Give the normal count of RBCs.

    Ans: In adult males: 4.5 – 6 (average 5.2) millions per cu mm of blood

    In adult females: 4 – 5.5 (average 4.7) millions per cu mm of blood

    In newborns: 6–8 millions per cu mm of blood

    In children: 3–5 millions per cu mm of blood

12. What are the proteins in red cell membrane?
Ans: Band-3 protein (chloride-bicarbonate exchanger), Glycophorins, Rh D protein, ankyrin and spectrin. The biconcave shape, deformability, membrane stability and durability of the red cells is due to ankyrin and spectrin.

13. What are the functions of red cells?
Ans: 1. Transport oxygen from lungs to the tissue by hemoglobin
2. Hemoglobins maintain acid base balance and transport carbon dioxide from tissues to lungs
3. RBCs contribute to 50% of viscosity of blood
4. Antigen on red cell membrane helps in blood group classification

14. List the steps of erythropoiesis.
Ans: Pluripotent stem cells → BFU-E → CFU-E → Pronormoblast → Basophilic erythroblast → Polychromatic erythroblast → Orthochromatic erythroblast → Reticulocyte → Erythrocyte

15. List the factors controlling erythropoiesis.
Ans: A. Hormonal factors (Stimulated by Erythropoietin, Androgens, Thyroxine, Growth hormone, Corticosteroid, Interleukins, TSH, ACTH, LH, FSH, Prolactin); Inhibited by Estrogen
B. Dietary factors (Vitamin B_{12}, folic acid, vitamin C), Proteins, Minerals (iron, copper, cobalt and nickel)
C. Other factors such as Intrinsic factor, Environmental factor (hypoxia), Chemical factors, Drugs

16. What is reticulocyte response?
Ans: When anemia is treated, increase in formation of RBCs occur and many reticulocytes are released into circulation increasing the reticulocyte count. This is called reticulocyte response.

17. List the conditions of increased and decreased RBC Count.
Ans: A. Conditions that decrease RBC count.
i) Physiological (Children, Women, Pregnancy)
ii) Pathological (Anemia, Excess ADH secretion)
B. Conditions that Increase RBC count
i) Physiological (High altitude, Newborns, Excessive sweating)
ii) Pathological (Polycythemia vera, diarrhea, vomiting, congenital heart disease, emphysema)

18. What are the types of hemoglobin?
Ans: Normal Hb (Adult Hb, Fetal Hb, Embryonic Hb)
Abnormal Hb (Hb S, Hb C, Hb D, Hb E, Unstable Hb)

19. What are the structures of various hemoglobins?
Ans: Adult Hb (Hb A - $\alpha_2\beta_2$ and Hb A_2 - $\alpha_2\delta_2$)
Fetal Hb (Hb F - $\alpha_2\gamma_2$)
Hb S: Valine replaces Glutamic acid at 6th position

20. List the functions of Hb.
Ans: 1. Transport of gasses: It transports oxygen from lungs to the tissues by forming *oxyhemoglobin* and carbon dioxide from tissues to lungs by forming *carbaminohemoglobin*.
When fully saturated, 1g of hemoglobin carries 1.34 ml of oxygen.
2. Hemoglobin buffer: Hb acts as a buffer to maintain blood pH.
3. Hb serves to destroy physiologically important nitric oxide molecule.
4. It imparts red color to the blood.

21. List the conditions of increased and decreased Hb level.
Ans: A. Conditions that decrease Hb Concentration
i) Physiological (Children, Women, Pregnancy)
ii) Pathological (Anemia, Excess ADH secretion)
B. Conditions that Increase Hb Concentration
i) Physiological (High altitude, Newborns, Excessive sweating)
ii) Pathological (Polycythemia vera, diarrhea, vomiting, congenital heart disease, emphysema)

22. Give the normal value of Hb.
Ans: Adult males: 14 to 18 (16 ± 2) g/dL of blood
Adult females: 12 to 16 (14 ± 2) g/dL of blood

23. Name some Hb-complexes
Ans: Oxyhemoglobin, Deoxygenated Hb, Nitrosohemoglobin, Carbaminohemoglobin, Carboxyhemoglobin, Methemoglobin, Sulfhemoglobin, Cyanmethemoglobin, and Glycated hemoglobins.

24. Give the etiological classification of anemia.
Ans:
A. Decreased red cell production (Aplastic anemia, Chronic renal failure, Megaloblastic anemia, Iron deficiency anemia, Thalassemia
B. Increased red cell destruction (Acute blood loss, Hypersplenism, Membrane defects, Enzyme defects)

25. Give the morphological classification of anemia.
Ans:
A. Hypochromic Microcytic Anemia (MCV, MCH, and MCHC are below normal) Iron deficiency anemia, *Thalassemia*
B. Normochromic Normocytic Anemia (MCV, MCH, and MCHC are normal) Blood loss, Hemolysis, Bone marrow failure, Chronic renal failure, Aplastic anemia
C. Macrocytic Normochromic Anemia (MCV is above normal) Megaloblastic anemia that due to deficiency of vitamin B_{12} or folic acid.

26. What is the Importance of Glycated Hb?
Ans: Glycated Hb is the measure of the degree of persistent hyperglycemia.

27. What is Sickle cell anemia?
Ans: Presence of abnormal hemoglobin called Hb S, in which glutamic acid is replaced by valine at the 6th position of beta chain. A hereditary disorder in which cells undergo intravascular hemolysis. The anemia is usually normochromic and normocytic.

28. What is Iron deficiency anemia?
Ans: This is the commonest form of anemia in the developing countries due to deficiency of iron. It is microcytic hypochromic type with decrease in all blood indices (MCV, MCH and MCHC). Deficiency of iron can be due to i) Increased physiological demand for iron as occurs in pregnancy, lactation, growing children; ii) Inadequate iron intake, as occurs due to deficiency in the diet iii) Pathological blood loss like bleeding peptic ulcer, piles, worm infestations, epistaxis, hemoptysis etc.

29. What is Hereditary Spherocytosis?
Ans: This is a hemolytic anemia due defect of red cell membrane that results in spherocytic shape of the cell and increased hemolysis. The anemia is normocytic and normochromic. There is increased osmotic fragility, hyperbilirubinemia, jaundice, enlarged spleen, and reticulocytosis.

30. What is thalassemia?
Ans: Thalassemia is a genetic disorder in which the rate of synthesis of hemoglobin chain is decreased, causing hemolytic anemia. There are two major classes: α thalassemia and β thalassemia. In **β thalassemia**, there is failure to synthesize β chain and excess α chain production. In **α** thalassemia, there is failure to synthesize α chain.

31. What is Polycythemia?
Ans: There is increase in number of red cells. The *primary form*, also called polycythemia vera is a neoplastic disorder of hematopoietic stem cells. The *secondary forms* are conditions of increased red cell production that usually occur due to appropriate or inappropriate increase in secretion of erythropoietin.

32. Classify Polycythemia
A. Primary polycythemia (Polycythemia vera)
B. Secondary polycythemia
i) Increase in erythropoietin secretion (High altitude, Congenital heart disease, Chronic lung diseases, Chronic smokers, Renal tumors, Liver tumors)
ii) Relative polycythemia (Dehydration)

33. What is the fate of destroyed red cells?
Ans: In the macrophages, red cells are degraded into lipids, protein and heme. Heme is catabolized to bilirubin, enters peripheral blood and circulate as unconjugated bilirubin.
Unconjugated bilirubin is transported to liver, gets conjugated and excreted through bile into the GI tract. In the intestine, bilirubin is converted to urobilinogen by bacterial reduction. Urobilinogen is further converted to stercobilinogen and stercobilin that are excreted in stool. A small fraction of urobilinogen is absorbed from intestine and excreted through urine as urinary urobilinogen.

34. What is physiological jaundice?
Ans: Hemolytic jaundice is seen in some newborns and therefore this is also known as neonatal jaundice. Normally, healthy liver can excrete a bilirubin load of six times of its normal concentration. However, in newborn as hepatic enzyme systems are not well developed, the bilirubin metabolism is not effective. Hence, hemolytic jaundice is common in them, and may become severe especially in premature deliveries.

35. What are the differences between different types of jaundice?
Ans:

	Hemolytic	**Hepatic**	**Obstructive**
Hyperbilirubinemia	Mild	Moderate	Severe
Fecal stercobilinogen	Increased	Decreased	Absent
Urinary urobilinogen	Increased	Decreased	Absent
Urinary bilirubin	Absent	Present	Present
Van den Bergh test	Indirect	Biphasic	Direct
Liver function	Normal	Impaired	May be impaired

Blood Groups and Physiological Basis of Blood Transfusion

36. Name some blood groups
Ans: ABO, Rh, MNS, P, Lutheran, Kell, Duffy, Kidd, Li, Lewis, Diego, Cartwright

37. What are the uses of blood groups
Ans: 1. Form the basis of compatibility testing for blood transfusion.
2. Provided the scientific basis for understanding hemolytic diseases of the newborn and autoimmune hemolytic anemias.
3. Play a critical role in susceptibility to infections by malaria parasites, bacteria and viruses.
4. Are associated with clinical disorders.
5. Are needed in establishing the identity of the father in cases of disputed paternities
6. Are believed to contribute to the personality of the individual.

38. What is Landsteiner's Law?
Ans: If a particular agglutinogen is present on the red cell membrane, the corresponding agglutinin is absent in plasma. Conversely, if the agglutinogen is absent in the red cells, the corresponding agglutinin is present in the plasma.

39. What are the blood groups and antigens in In ABO system?
Ans: There are two antigens (agglutinogens) A and B, two antibodies (agglutinins) A and B. Based on this, there are four blood groups.
Group A : Antigen A is present, antibody B is present
Group B : Antigen B is present, antibody A is present
Group AB: Both A and B antigens are present, No antibody
Group O: No antigen, Both A and B antibodies are present

40. What is Rh system?
Ans: In Rh system, there are six antigens, C, D, E, c, d and e, but no naturally occurring antibodies. The most active is the D antigen. Thus, in Rh system, there are two blood groups: Rh positive (D antigen present) and Rh negative (D antigen absent).

41. What is Erythroblastosis Fetalis?

Ans: This is a hemolytic disease of the newborn due to Rh incompatibility when an Rh negative mother carries Rh positive fetus during pregnancy.

Usually, no reaction occurs in the first pregnancy. However, at the time of delivery during placental separation, a small amount of fetal blood leaks into the maternal circulation. This induces formation of anti-Rh antibodies in the mother.

In subsequent pregnancies, the anti-Rh antibodies from mother, which is predominantly IgG type crosses placenta to enter the fetal circulation and causes hemolysis.

In third and subsequent pregnancies, the degree of hemolysis becomes severe.

42. What are the clinical features of erythroblastosis fetalis?

Ans: Anemia, Hemolytic jaundice, Edema (due to anemia and hypoproteinemia, called hydrops fetalis), Hyperbilirubinemia, Kernicterus (due to the deposition of bilirubin in the basal ganglia), Erythroblasts (nucleated red cells) in peripheral blood.

43. How erythroblastosis fetalis can be prevented?

Ans: By administering a single dose of anti-Rh antibodies during the post-partum period following the first delivery. The disease can also be prevented by giving Rh immunoglobulins during pregnancy.

44. How erythroblastosis fetalis can be treated?

Ans: i) Intrauterine fetal transfusion ii) Exchange transfusion with ABO negative red cells. iii) **Phototherapy**

45. What are the Indications for blood transfusion?

Ans:

i) Acute blood loss, ii) Chronic anemia, iii) Bone marrow failure, iv) Purpura, v) Clotting factor deficiencies, vi) Preparation for surgery and during surgery, vii) Burns, viii) Anemia

46. What is major cross-matching?

Ans: The cells of the donor are matched against the plasma of the recipient.

47. What is minor cross-matching?

Ans: The donor's plasma is matched against the red cells of the recipient.

48. What are the hazards of blood transfusion?

Ans:

i) Due to Mismatched Transfusion: Shivering and fever, Hemolytic jaundice, Hemoglobinemia and hemoglobinuria, Acute renal failure, Hyperkalemia
ii) **Due to Faulty Techniques of Giving Blood: Thrombophlebitis:** Air Embolism
iii) Due to Massive Transfusion: Cardiac arrhythmias or cardiac arrest occur due to high potassium level in the stored blood.
iv) Febrile Reaction due to presence of pyrogens in the transfusion apparatus.
v) Allergic Reactions: Itching, erythema, nausea, vomiting, anaphylactic reactions.
vi) Transmission of Diseases: Hepatitis, Malaria, AIDS, Syphilis

White Blood Cells and Immunity

49. What are the Granulocytes and Agranulocytes

Ans: Granulocytes (Neutrophils, Eosinphils, Basophils)
Agranulocytes (Monocytes, Lymphocytes)

50. What are the distribution of leucocytes in peripheral blood

Neutrophils (50 – 70%) ; Eosinophils (1 – 4%); Basophils (0 – 1%); Monocytes (2 – 8%); Lymphocytes (20 – 40%)

51. What are the phases in the life of a leucocyte?

Ans: Three phases: marrow phase, circulatory phase and tissue phase.

i) In the marrow phase (6 to 10 days): Develop from progenitor cells, grow into mature leucocytes and get released into circulation.
ii) In the circulatory phase (6 to 8 hours) Circulate in the blood vessels
iii) In the tissue phase (4 to 5 days): They enter the tissues.

52. What is Barr body?

Ans: In females, in about 30% of neutrophils, sex chromatin is present as a drumstick appendage (about 1 μm) attached to the nucleus by a thin chromatin strand. This is known as Barr body. It helps to determination the gender of the individual.

53. What are the identifying features of a neutrophil?

Ans: Size is10–14 μm, Cytoplasm contains fine pink colored granules, Nucleus is usually multilobed and the lobes are connected by thin strand.

54. What are the conditions of neutrophilia?

Ans:

i) Acute conditions: Acute bacterial infections, burn, infarction, trauma, electric shock, gout, exercise, cold, pain, labor, surgery, panic, severe stress, depression, epinephrine, glucocorticoids, vaccines

ii) Chronic chonditions: Pancreatitis, myositis, colitis, rheumatoid arthritis, ACTH excess, thyroid storm, tumors (Gastric, renal, bronchial and hepatic), chronic hemolysis, meyloproliferative diseases

55. What are the conditions of neutropenia?

Ans: Typhoid and paratyphoid fevers, malaria, kala azar, aplastic anemia, measles, influenza, hypersplenism, systemic lupus erythematosus, Drugs (Chloramphenicol, phenylbutazone, phenytoin

56. What are the functions of neutrophil?

Ans: Neutrophils are considered as the first line of defense against acute bacterial infections. It is actively phagocytic.

57. What are the phagocytic cells ?

Ans: Neutrophils, Monocytes and Macrophages

58. What are the steps of neutrophil phagocytosis?
Ans: Chemotaxis, Diapedesis, Opsonization and Adherence, Ingestion and Killing
Chemotaxis: It is the process of migration of neutrophils to the site of infection. Complement proteins, especially C5a and C3 also act as chemotaxins.
Diapedesis: Neutrophils pass through the capillary endothelial cells to reach the invader in the tissue.
Opsonization: The process by which the bacteria are made tasty to the phagocyte is called opsonization. The bacteria is coated by opsonins, such as IgG, C5a, C3b.
Adherence: Bacteria coated by opsonins bind to the receptor on the neutrophil membrane.
Ingestion: The membrane of phagocyte extends pseudopodia to surround the microbe and form phagocytic vesicle.
Killing: Neutrophil granules contain degradative enzymes, proteases, defensins and cationic proteins that kill the microbe (non-oxidative mechanism) and produce a number of oxygen metabolites that are antimicrobial (non-oxidative mechanism)

59. What are the identifying features of an eosinophil?
Ans: Size is10–14 µm, Cytoplasm contains coarse and brick red granules, Nucleus is usually bilobed and the lobes are separated by a thick strand (Spectacles appearance).

60. What are the functions of eosinophil?
Ans: Eosinophils act against helminthic infections and allergy.

61. What are the contents of granules of eosinophil?
Ans: Major basic protein, Eosinophil cationic protein, Eosinophil-derived peroxidase, Eosinophil-derived neurotoxin, Interleukins (IL1-6, IL8 and IL12), Lysophospholipase, Phospholipase D, Arylsulphatase-B, Acid phosphatase, Catalase and Histaminase

62. What are the conditions of eosinophilia?
Ans: Helminthic infections (Roundworm, Filariasis, Hookworm), Asthma, Allergic rhinitis, Food allergy, Hay fever, Urticaria, Atopic dermatitis, Eosinophilic leukemia, Tropical pulmonary eosinophilia, Addison's disease

63. What are the conditions of eosinopenia?
Ans: Aplastic anemia, Glucocorticoid therapy, Cushing's syndrome

64. What are basophils and their functions?
Ans: Size is 10 – 14 µm, Nucleus often appear 'S' shaped, Granules are large in size, more in number, secrete histamine that causes vasodilation.

65. What are the conditions of basophilia?
Ans: Allergic and inflammatory conditions (Ulcerative colitis, Urticaria, Drug and food hypersensitivity), Infections (Chicken pox, Small pox, Influenza, Tuberculosis), Myxedema (hypothyroidism), Diabetes mellitus, Iron deficiency, Basophilic leukemia, Polycythemia

66. What are the conditions of basopenia?
Ans: Cortisol therapy, Cushing's syndrome, Hyperthyroidism, Ovulation, Hypersensitivity reactions.

67. What are the functions of Monocyte?
Ans: Monocyte is the second line of defense against infections. Main functions are phagocytosis and microbial killing, also kill intracellular pathogens like viruses, and parasites, antigen presentation, release of cytokines like IL-1, IL-6, TNF-α and interferons, growth factors like GM-CSF, M-CSF, TGF, PDGF and FGF.

68. What are the conditions of monocytopenia?
Ans: Aplastic anemia, Hairy cell leukemia, Septicemia

69. What are Mast cells and their functions?
Ans: Mast cells are derived from blood precursors, but they mainly reside in the connective tissues. They have high-affinity receptors for IgE on their surface, mediate many allergic responses of the body, secrete histamine, heparin.

70. What are the conditions of monocytosis?
Ans: Acute monocytic leukemia, Hodgkin's disease, Polycythemia vera, Hemolytic anemia, Splenectomy, Cytomegalovirus infection, Malaria, Kala azar, Glucocorticoid therapy, Collagen diseases, Chronic idiopathic monocytosis

71. What are Macrophages and their functions?
Ans: Monocytes after their life span in blood enter tissues and transform into tissue macrophages. They form mononuclear phagocyte system in various tissues. Size: 25 to 50 µm, contain multiple large azurophil granules. In chronic tissue inflammations, macrophages are converted into multinucleated giant cells that are highly phagocytic and microbicidal.

72. What are the important cells of mononuclear phagocyte system?
Ans: Kupffer cells of the liver, Alveolar macrophages in the lungs, Microglia of brain, Tissue macrophages in the spleen and lymph nodes, Osteoclasts in bone, Mesangial cells in kidney, Histiocytes in connective tissues, Langerhans cells in the skin

73. What are the Macrophages and their functions?
Ans: Few monocytes are transformed into highly specialized mononuclear cells called dendritic cells. They play important role in antigen processing and presentation to the T cells. They are present in blood and bone marrow, present as Langerhans cells in skin, interdigitating cells in thymic medulla, and interstitial cells in the lung and heart.

74. What are the lymphocytes and their functions?
Ans: Lymphocytes are B cells, T cells and NK cells. B cells mediate humoral immunity. T cells mediate cellular immunity. NK cells mediate natural and nonspecific immunity.

75. What are the conditions of Lymphocytosis?
Ans: Lmphocytic leukemia, Infectious mononucleosis, Bordetella pertusis, Tuberculosis, Splenectomy, Cigarette smoking, Septic shock

76. What are the conditions of Lymphocytopenia?
Ans: Aplastic anemia, AIDS, Hepatitis, Glucocorticoid therapy, Typhoid fever, Systemic lupus erythematosus

77. What is leukemia?
Ans: Leukemia is defined as a malignant neoplasia of hemopoietic cells in which there is abnormal proliferation of leucocytes and their precursors resulting in appearance of abnormal and immature cells in the peripheral blood associated with very high leucocytosis, and infiltration of tissues by leukemic cells.

78. What are the types of leukemia?
Ans: Acute and chronic myeloid (myelocytic) leukemia; Acute and chronic lymphocytic leukemia.

79. What are the features of leukemia?
Ans: Very high leucocytosis, Abnormal and immature cells in the peripheral blood, Anemia, Weight loss, Weakness, Easy fatigability, Hepatomegaly, Splenomegaly, Lymphadenopathy.

80. What are the functions of thymus?
Ans: ThethymusisthesiteforTcelldevelopment.Thymectomyinyoung leads to depletion of T cells and immunodeficiency within few months.

81. What are the functions of spleen?
Ans:
1. Spleen is the site for production of B and T cells, thus, has important role in immunity.
2. Spleen removes old and abnormal red cells, white cells and platelets.
3. Spleen helps in hepatic stage of hemopoiesis during intrauterine life.
4. Spleen acts as an important reservoir of blood in mammals.
5. Macrophages in spleen recycle iron, which has been released from destroyed red cells.

82. What are the types of immunity?
Ans:
A. Innate (non-adaptive) immunity (Nonspecific defenses, NK cells)
B. Acquired (adaptive) immunity
1. Naturally acquired
a) Active immunity (Cellular immunity, Humoral immunity)
b) Passive (Ig G via placenta, Ig A via breast feeding)
2. Artificially acquired
a) Active immunity (vaccination)
b) Passive immunity (anti-D immunization of Rh –ve mother)

83. What are the types of T cells and their functions?
Ans: Helper T cells (T4 cells), Cytotoxic T cells (T_8 cells), and Memory T cells.

84. What are the steps of cellular immunity?
Ans: Mechanism of cellular immunity includes following steps:
i) Antigen recognition, processing and presentation: On entry into the body, the antigen is recognized by the T or B cell. For B cell, the antigen binds to the specific receptor present on the B cell surface. For T cell, the antigen presenting cells (APCs: macrophages, dendritic cells and B cells) process and present the antigens to the T cells. The steps of antigen presentation are ingestion of antigens, digestion of antigen, fusion of vesicles, binding of peptide fragments to MHC molecule, and incorporation of antigen-MHC complex into the cell membrane of APC.
ii) Activation and proliferation of T cells: When the receptors on the T cell surface (TCR) come in contact with MHC-antigen complex located on the surface of the APCs, T cells are activated. The activated T cells with co-stimulation by inducer cells (type 1 Helper Cells), undergo proliferation and differentiation into two sets of T cells: the cytotoxic T cells, and the memory T cells.
iii) Elimination of the invader: The cytotoxic T cells kill the invading microbes by cytolysis (cytotoxic T cells cells synthesize and secrete perforins, and incorporate them into the membranes of the invading organisms, causing osmotic lysis), by secretion of Lymphotoxins like Tumor necrosis factor β (TNF-β), and by Interferons (Cytotoxic T cells secrete gamma-interferons that kill the viruses).

85. What are the pathogens against which cellular immunity works?
Ans: Viral and fungal infections, cancer cells, transplanted cells, chronic bacterial infections like tuberculosis, brucellosis, and parasitic infections.

86. What are the steps of humoral immunity?
Ans:
i) Activation of B cells: by binding of antigen to the B cell receptors
ii) Differentiation of B cells into plasma cells: The activated B cell enlarges in size and undergoes differentiation to become plasma cell. Co-stimulation from type 2 helper cells that secrete IL-2, IL-4, and IL-5, facilitates.
iii) Proliferation of plasma cells and production of antibodies (Immunoglobulins G,A,M,D,E)
iv) Killing of the invaders by antibodies by neutralizing antigen, immobilization of microbes, activation of complement system, precipitation of antigens and facilitation of phagocytosis
v) Formation of memory B cells and subsequent immunological responses

87. What are the types of humoral immune response?
Ans: Two types: primary and secondary
i) Primary response: When antigen enters into the body for the first time, the immune response induced is called primary response. The antibodies are formed slowly with a latent period of about four days to four weeks. The concentration of antibodies, mainly IgM,

rises gradually and attains a smaller peak. Then antibody titer returns back to normal within few days to weeks.

ii) Secondary response: When the same antigen enters the body for the second time (or on subsequent exposure), the immune response triggered is the secondary response. It occurs speedily and intensely, which is due to the immunological memory (memory B and T cells). Concentration of antibody (primarily of IgG type) rises fast and reaches a greater peak, then the antibody titer falls very slowly and never returns to normal.

88. What are the functions of complements?
Ans: They activates B cell, promote opsonization and phagocytosis. Following apoptosis, complement proteins help in disposing the debris.

89. What are the functions of antibodies?
Ans: IgG: Complement fixation by classical pathway
IgA: Localized protection in body secretions like tear, salivary and intestinal secretions, etc.; complement fixation by alternate pathway
IgM: Complement fixation by classical pathway
IgD: Antigen recognition by B cells
IgE: Histamine releases from mast cells and basophils; also has reagin activity

90. What is immunological tolerance (or self-recognition)?
Ans: The unresponsiveness of the individual to self antigen. The individual's own MHC proteins do not recognize self-antigens, thus do not react against them to form antibodies. Fetal tolerance is an example of immunological tolerance.

91. What is the mechanism of immunological tolerance (or self-recognition)?
Ans: It is based on the process of negative and positive selections.
Negative selections: During the process of development of T cells in thymus, T cells with receptors that recognize self- MHC molecules are eliminated while T cells with receptors that do not recognize self-MHC molecules are retained. This occurs either due to clonal deletion (the self-reactive T cells undergo apoptosis) or clonal anergy (the self-reactive T cells remain unresponsive to immunologic stimulation).
Positive selections: T cells that are capable of recognizing self-MHC molecules during their thymic development survive and those that do not recognize undergo apoptosis. The T cells recognize MHC- self antigen complex as the self-antigens and do not react against them.

92. What is Transplant rejection and how to prevent it?
Ans: The immune system recognizes the transplanted tissue as a foreign organ and activation of cellular immunity finally rejects the tissue. It is prevented by immunosuppressive drugs (azathioprine), Glucocorticoid therapy, Antilymphocyte globulins, Antibiotics (Cyclosporine, Tacrolimus, Rapamycin) and monoclonal antibodies.

Platelets (Thrombocytes)

93. Define hemostasis.
Ans: The process of arrest of bleeding while maintaining blood in a fluid state within the vascular system.

94. What is temporary (primary) hemostasis?
Ans: The initial stage during which vascular wall and platelet interact to limit the blood loss from damaged vessel is known as temporary hemostasis.

95. What is definitive (secondary) hemostasis?
Ans: It is the stage when a stable fibrin clot is formed from clotting factors by enzymatic reactions. This finally stops the bleeding.

96. What are the steps of hemostasis?
Ans: Three stages: vasoconstriction, temporary hemostatic plug formation and blood coagulation.
i) Vasoconstriction: Immediate response of blood vessel to injury is vasoconstriction. It is maintained by secretion of serotonin from the activated platelets.
ii) Hemostatic plug formation: Formation of platelet plug at the site of injury by adhesion, aggregation, activation of platelets and release of chemicals from platelets.
iii) Blood coagulation: The activation of clotting factors results in formation of blood clot at the site of injury that stops bleeding.

97. What are the properties of platelets?
Ans: Platelets have three properties: adhesion, aggregation, and activation & release.
Adhesion: Platelets adhere to the exposed collagen of the injured vessel wall. This is facilitated by von Willebrand factor
Aggregation: The property of platelets to stick to each other is called platelet aggregation. Fibrinogen and GpIIb-IIIa, thrombin, ADP and PAF promote platelet aggregation.
Activation & release: Platelets are activated when they bind to collagen or to each other. The activation is facilitated by thrombin and ADP. The activated platelets change their shape and discharge their granular contents called platelet release.

98. What are the functions of platelets?
Ans: 1. Temporary hemostasis: Platelets form plugs at the site of injury, called temporary hemostatic plug. Platelets also promote vasoconstriction by producing serotonin that helps in hemostasis.
2. Blood coagulation: Platelets release platelet factor 4, and synthesize clotting factor V and XI.
3. Clot retraction: Platelets promote clot retraction, which is essential for stabilization of clot.
4. Thrombolysis: Platelet controls fibrinolysis.
5. Phagocytosis: Platelets phagocytose smaller molecules like immune complexes and viruses.
6. Storage and transport: Platelets synthesize, secrete and transport many chemical substances, such as serotonin, ADP, calcium, von Willebrand factor etc.
7. Vascular growth: Platelets help in growth of vascular endothelium by secreting platelet–derived growth factor.

99. What are the platelet functions tests?
Ans: Platelet count, Bleeding time, Platelet aggregation tests, Platelet adhesiveness test, Clot retraction time

100. What is the normal count and conditions of altered count of platelets?

Ans: Normal count: 1.5–4 lakhs/mm3 of blood.

Thrombocytopenia: Idiopathic thrombocytopenic purpura, aplastic anemia, hypersplenism, acute leukemia, cytotoxic chemotherapy and radiation.

Critical count: Platelet count below 50,000/mm^3 of blood is called critical count as significant bleeding occurs at this count.

Thrombocytosis: Essential thrombocythemia, Polycythemia rubra vera, Chronic myeloid leukemia, Acute blood loss, Iron deficiency, After splenectomy, Malignancies, Drugs (vincristine, epinephrine), After surgery, Chronic infection

101. What is idiopathic thrombocytopenic purpura?

Ans: A primary autoimmune purpura characterized by thrombocytopenia which is due to formation of antibody against platelets. It is treated by corticosteroids and splenectomy.

102. What are the clotting factors?

Ans: Factor I (Fibrinogen). Factor II (Prothrombin), Factor III (Tissue thromboplastin), Factor IV (Calcium ion), Factor V (Proaccelerin), Factor VII (Proconvertin), Factor VIII (Antihemophilic factor A), Factor IX (Christmas factor or Antihemophilic factor B), Factor X (Stuart Prower factor), Factor XI (Plasma thromboplastin antecedent, or Antihemophilic factor C), Factor XII (Hageman factor or contact factor), Factor XIII (Fibrin stabilizing factor or, Laki-Lorand factor)

103. What is the intrinsic pathway of blood coagulation?

Ans: It occurs in three stages.

Stage 1: Activation of Stuart-Prower factor (formation of prothrombin activator): When factor XII comes in contact with exposed collagen, it gets activated, and then it activates factor XI. Then activated factor XI activates factor IX in presence of calcium. Then activated factor IX activates factor X in presence of activated factor VIII, calcium and membrane phospholipid.

Stage 2: Formation of thrombin from prothrombin: The activated factor X converts prothrombin to thrombin in presence of activated factor V, calcium and platelet phospholipid.

Stage 3: Formation of fibrin from fibrinogen: Thrombin converts fibrinogen to fibrin, which gets stabilized by Fibrin stabilizing factor.

104. What is the extrinsic pathway of blood coagulation?

Ans: Release of tissue thromboplastin (TPL) from the injured tissue activates factor VII, which then activates factor X in presence of calcium, platelet phospholipid and TPL. Then the activated factor X converts prothrombin to thrombin in presence of activated factor V, calcium and platelet phospholipid. Then thrombin converts fibrinogen to fibrin, which gets stabilized by Fibrin stabilizing factor.

105. What is Clot retraction?

Ans: When blood is allowed to clot in a test tube, within minutes to hours, clot shrinks expressing serum out of it. This phenomenon is called clot retraction.

106. What is the mechanism of clot retraction?

Ans: Within the clot, the platelets form filopodia that extend along the fibrin threads. Fibrin strands tug with the filopodia. Later, platelets shrink with contraction of their filopodia. This causes internalization of fibrin within the contracted platelets. Thus, retraction of clot occurs.

107. What are the functions of clot retraction?

Ans: Retracted clot (thrombus) strongly seals injured vessel, facilitates wound healing and prevents thrombolysis.

108. What is the mechanism of fibrinolysis (thrombolysis)?

Ans: Thrombin, in presence of thrombomodulin activates protein C, which then activates plasminogen activator that forms plasmin from plasminogen. Plasmin causes lysis of fibrin.

Also, activated protein C with protein S inactivates activated factor V and VIII, thus preventing coagulation.

109. What are the vitamin K-dependent clotting factors?

Ans: Factors II, VII, IX and X

110. What are the vitamin K-antagonists, and their mechanism of action ?

Ans: Warfarin, Dicoumarol. They inhibit γ-carboxylation of factors II, VII, IX and X, thus, significantly impairing their coagulation activity.

111. What is hemophilia ?

Ans: Hemophilia A, also known as classic hemophilia, is a bleeding disorder due to deficiency of factor VIII, an X-linked recessive hereditary disease, women are carriers. The features are bleeding, hematomas, hemarthroses and crippling hemarthropathy. Assay of factor VIII in plasma is diagnostic. The treatment consists of transfusion of fresh blood or transfusion of factor VIII-concentrate.

112. What is Christmas disease ?

Ans: Christmas disease or hemophilia-B occurs due to deficiency of factor-IX. This is a sex-linked recessive hemorrhagic disease. The features are bleeding, hematomas, hemarthroses and crippling hemarthropathy. Assay of factor IX in plasma is diagnostic. The treatment is transfusion of transfusion of factor IX-concentrate.

113. What is von Willebrand disease ?

Ans: It is an inherited bleeding disorder due to deficiency of von Willebrand factor (vWF). Features are mucocutaneous bleeding, epistaxis, easy bruising, hematoma and GI bleeding. There is prolongation of bleeding time. Assays of plasma vWF is diagnostic. Treated by Desmopressin and replacement of vWF.

114. What is Disseminated Intravascular Coagulation (DIC) ?

Ans: In DIC, there is widespread intravascular coagulation that occurs due to procoagulants. Also known as consumption coagulopathy or defibrination syndrome. The common causes of DIC are septic abortions, severe trauma, eclampsia, burns. There is bleeding with multiorgan dysfunctions caused by widespread microembolism. There is thrrombocytopenia, hypofibrinogenemia, increased d-dimer and fibrin degradation product in urine. Treatment is based on elimination of the precipitating factors, and replacing coagulation factors and platelets.

SECTION III-NERVE AND MUSCLE

MULTIPLE CHOICE QUESTIONS

1. Voltage-gated sodium channels are vital to the functioning of the nervous system. Which of the following statements is true in order for a voltage-gated sodium channel to open?
   A. The 'ball and chain' needs to be positively charged
   B. The four pore loops need to move inwards
   C. The four pore loops need to move outwards
   D. The four S4 segments need to move outwards
   E. The four S4 segments need to move inwards

2. Ion channels are frequently formed by the interaction of several sub-units, each having a number of membrane-spanning segments. How many primary sub-units combine together to form the sodium channel found in nerves?
   A. 2 B. 3 **C. 4**
   D. 5 E. 6

3. There are two principal cell types specific to the nervous system: neurones that are excitable cells which process and transmit information, and glial cells that serve a variety of supporting roles. Which of the following statements about neurones is true?
   A. There are fewer neuroglial cells than neurones
   B. Nissl bodies contain endoplasmic reticulum
   C. Nerve impulses are conducted from the neurone via the dendrites
   D. There is usually one dendrite per neurone
   E. Dendrites play an important role in neuronal transport

4. The two principal cell types of the nervous system are neurones and glial cells. Glial cells are smaller, consisting of astrocytes, oligodendrocytes and Schwann cells, and microglia. What are the functions of astrocytes?
   A. Form myelin sheaths
   B. Immunological defence
   C. Transmit signals
   D. Formation of new blood vessels
   E. Ion homeostasis

5. Astrocytes contribute to maintaining the extracellular environment of the CNS through:
   A. Capture and redistribution of excess K+ and other ions
   B. Enveloping extensions of its cytoplasm around the axons
   C. Phagocytosis of injured CNS neurons
   D. Lining of the ventricular surface of the CNS
   E. Differentiation to neurons in response to injury

6. Dermatomyositis is an autoimmune disorder in which chronic peripheral vascular inflammation is observed. In which connective tissue layer will you see these chronic inflammatory cells?
   A. Aponeurosis **B. Perimysium** C. Epimysium
   D. Sarcoplasma E. Basal sheet

7. A tired soldier, on guard, standing in the rain, begins to feel sleepy and his legs give way. Out of reflex he contracts the quadriceps and returns to the attention position. His quadriceps contracted because the sensory neuron alpha IA that innervates the fibers _____ perceived the change in length of his muscle and sent a reflex to the motor neuron alpha A on the _____ side to contract and stop the change in length.
   A. Intrafusals of the muscle spindle, ipsilateral
   B. Intrafusals of the muscle spindle, contralateral
   C. Extrafusals of the muscle spindle, ipsilateral
   D. Extrafusals of the muscle spindle, contralateral
   E. From the Golgi tendon organ, ipsilateral

8. 1.A patient presents to the neurology clinic with muscle weakness of recent onset. Neurological examination reveals weakness in all limbs, which worsens as the limb is exercised. Cranial nerve examination reveals drooping eyelids, the droop becoming more severe after the patient is asked to raise her eyelids for 1 minute. After discussion of the case, a chest X-ray is ordered. What condition is being sought that would account for the patient's weakness?
   A. Patchy bronchopneumonia
   B. Left ventricular hypertrophy
   C. Thymic hyperplasia
   D. Air below the left hemidiaphragm
   E. Rib fracture

9. The action potential of a motor neuron cannot be initiated for contraction of an innervated skeletal muscle in the absence of extracellular Ca^{++} due to:
   A. The inhibition of the uptake of Ca^{++} in the innervated muscle
   B. The inhibition of acetylcholine binding to motor end-plate receptors
   C. The stimulation of acetylcholine degradation
   D. The inhibition of the release of acetylcholine from the motor neuron
   E. The inhibition of the Ca^{++} binding to troponin C in the innervated muscle

10. The length constant for passive conduction of a depolarization increases as the diameter of a non-myelinated axon increases. This is mainly due to:
   A. Increased membrane capacitance
   B. Decreased membrane capacitance
   C. Increased membrane resistance
   D. Decreased membrane resistance
   E. Decreased axoplasmic resistance

11. A 24-year-old medical student goes to the gym to do weights. As a warm-up, she starts by lifting 50 kg on the bench, then gradually increases the weight. Which of the following processes takes place as she adds more weight?
   A. Decreased frequency of motor nerve action potentials

B. Decreased speed of the motor nerve action potentials
C. Increased frequency of motor nerve action potentials
D. Increased speed of motor nerve action potentials
E. Affected motor units are scarce

12. A 24-year-old woman enters the emergency department after a traffic accident in which she suffered lacerations to her left wrist and severed an important tendon. The ends of the tendon had been superimposed 6 cm to facilitate suturing and reinsertion. Which of the following should be expected after 6 weeks compared to the muscle before the injury? Suppose that the serial growth of sarcomeres cannot be completed in that time frame. Passive tension Maximum active tension Option 1 Decreases Decreases Option 2 Decreases Increases Option 3 Increases Increases Option 4 Increases Decreases Option 5 No change No change
A. Option 1 B. Option 2 C. Option 3
D. Option 4 E. Option 5

13. A 45-year-old male goes to the gym to lift weights. As a warm-up, start by lifting on the bench 65 kg, and then gradually increase the weight. Which of the following groups of changes occurs when you add more weight? Activation of motor units Frequency of motor nerve action potentials Option 1 Decreases Decreases Option 2 Decreases Increases Option 3 Decreases No change Option 4 Increases Decreases Option 5 IncreasesIncreases Option 6IncreasesNo change
A. Option 1 B. Option 2 C. Option 3
D. Option 4 **E. Option 5** F. Option 6

14. The pre-synaptic nerve terminal plays a role in the releasing of synaptic vesicles, which are involved in cellular signalling. At a pre-synaptic nerve terminal, the release of synaptic vesicles relies mainly on which of the following options?
A. Entry of sodium ion B. Exit of potassium ions
C. Entry of calcium ions D. Entry of magnesium ions
E. Entry of chloride ions

15. The giant squid axon was studied extensively in the 1900s. Which one of the following substances can be used to block the early inward current seen when depolarizing squid giant axons using the voltage-clamp?
A. $Zn2^+$ **B. TTX** C. TEA
D. Botulinum toxin E. Curare

16. A 25-year-old pregnant woman presents with increased muscle weakness, double vision and drooping eyelids.What is the most likely diagnosis for this patient?
A. Carpal tunnel syndrome B. Parkinson's disease
C. Multiple sclerosis D. Subarachnoid haemorrhage
E. Myasthenia gravis

17. A 52-year-old woman with chronic myaesthenia gravis is admitted to hospital with severe urinary sepsis. She is transferred to the Intensive Care Unit and commenced on fluids and an aminoglycoside antibiotic. Her blood pressure initially improves but 4 hours later she has a respiratory arrest and requires ventilation.What is the most likely cause, from the list below, of this patient's weakness?
A. Botulinum toxin
B. Gentamycin
C. Penicillamine
D. Magnesium
E. Organophosphate

18. A 62-year-old type 1 diabetic patient with vitiligo develops progressive weakness over the course of 2 months. It affects her proximal muscles and is worse at night. She finds that when she reads for a long time, she develops drooping eyelids and double vision, however, all her symptoms are fully resolved when she wakes up in the morning. She undergoes a nerve conduction study which shows a decremental response to repetitive stimulation and she tests positive for acetylcholine receptor antibodies.What is the most likely cause, from the list below, of this patient's weakness?
A. Motor neurone disease
B. Guillain–Barré syndrome
C. Myaesthenia gravis
D. Multiple sclerosis
E. Lambert–Eaton myasthenic syndrome (LEMS)

19. A 59-year-old college professor goes to his doctor for muscle fatigue that worsens at the end of the day. The doctor notes that the patient has drooping eyelids and appears to show generalized weakness in all muscles. After intravenous administration of Tensilon®, which blocks the degradation of acetylcholine, the eyelid drooping and symptoms of muscle weakness appear to remit. Which of the following diagnoses best reflects the patient's condition?
A. Encephalitis B. Fibromyalgia
C. Flaccid paralysis **D. Myasthenia gravis**
E. Poliomyelitis

20. A 10-year-old father and daughter die suddenly from drowning after eating smoked white fish from the Great Lakes. Three other members of the family have fallen ill, suffering from dry mouth despite drinking large amounts of liquids. His upper eyelids are drooping. Vision is clear, but pupils are dilated and do not respond to light. Two of them need assisted ventilation. Botulism (Clostridium botulinum) is suspected. Surviving patients begin to improve as soon as they receive the only treatment available, antitoxin E. The deadly effect of botulinum toxin occurs because:
B. Decreases norepinephrine release
A. Decreases the release of acetylcholine
C. Exhaust calcium reserves in the muscle
D. Causes tetany in skeletal muscle
E. Stimulates ryanodine receptors

21. A 3-day-old infant is evaluated for poor feeding, hypotonia, dyspnea, weak crying and ptosis. He is the product of a full-term pregnancy and was born vaginally without complications. The boy's mother was scheduled for a thymectomy for muscle weakness, dysphagia, double vision and ptosis. Despite adequate treatment, including

anticholinesterase therapy, the patient died of respiratory failure at 6 days of age. What is the most likely diagnosis?

A. Lambert–Eaton myasthenic syndrome (LEMS)

B. Neonatal myasthenia gravis

C. Infantile botulism

D. Guillain-Barré syndrome

E. Multiple sclerosis

22. The «calcium influx factor», or CIF, is a factor that:

A. Is released by the endothelial cells to favor the contraction of the adjacent smooth muscle

B. Facilitates the filling of Ca^{++} in the sarcoplasmic reticulum by favoring the localized entry of Ca^{++} into the cell

C. It is necessary for the activation of the channels of Ca++ activated by voltage in the smooth muscle

D. Facilitates smooth muscle contraction by increasing the cytosolic concentration of Ca^{++}

E. Promotes smooth muscle relaxation by inducing sparkles of Ca^{++}

23. Which of the following best describes the source of ATP in the skeletal muscle during prolonged anaerobic exercise?

A. Beta-oxidation of fats

B. Glycolysis

C. Muscle reserve of ATP

D. Phosphocreatine

E. Protein hydrolysis

24. Which of the following energy sources is most likely to be used first during an exhausting burst of activity in a normal skeletal muscle fiber?

A. Adenosine triphosphate

B. Anaerobic glycolysis

C. Lactate oxidation

D. Phosphocreatine

E. Fatty acids

25. A 28-year-old male has been training as a long-distance runner for the past six years. Compared to a sprinter, which of the following parameters will be diminished in the skeletal muscle of this athlete under resting conditions?

A. Capillary blood flow

B. Glycolytic enzyme content

C. Mitochondrial volume density

D. Myoglobin , content

E. Oxidative capacity

26. A physiology experiment records muscle contraction against a force transducer without decreasing the muscle length. What type of muscular contraction is occurring?

A. Isometric contraction

B. Isotonic contraction

C. Twitch

D. Treppe

E. Tetany

27. During exercise, skeletal muscle may release local factors, such as adenosine, which can relax the neighboring vascular smooth muscle and thus promote vasodilation in the muscle being exercised. The mechanism by which adenosine promotes the relaxation of smooth muscle usually involves:

A. Inhibition of K^+ channels in vascular smooth muscle

B. Stimulation of InsP3 production in vascular smooth muscle

C. Stimulation of endothelin release from adjacent endothelial cells

D. Stimulation of cAMP production (adenylyl cyclase mechanism) in vascular smooth muscle

E. Activation of the channels of Ca^{++} activated by voltage in the vascular smooth muscle

28. The ability to increase strength in an intact muscle formed by fast-contracting and slow-contracting muscle fibers usually involves:

A. The intake of slow-contracting muscle fibers before fast-contracting muscle fibers

B. Tetany in the fast-contracting muscle at lower stimulation frequencies than a slow-contracting muscle

C. The intake of more muscle fibers in a given motor unit

D. The progressive increase in the amplitude of intracellular Ca++ transient currents

E. The progressive reduction of the threshold for an action potential in the skeletal muscle

29. Resistance training usually increases:

A. The uptake of Ca^{++} in the muscle fiber

B. The oxidative capacity of the muscle

C. The conversion of the slow-contracting muscle into a fast contracting muscle

D. The number of muscle fibers in a muscle

E. The output of Ca^{++} from the muscle fiber

30. There may be an increase in smooth muscle tension to a given intracellular [Ca^{++}] in response to:

A. Opening of the K^+ channels in the smooth muscle membrane

B. Inhibition of myosin phosphatase by Rho kinase in smooth muscle,

C. cAMP dependent phosphorylation of myosin light chain kinase in smooth muscle

D. Release of nitric oxide by adjacent endothelial cells

E. Hyperpolarization of the smooth muscle membrane

31. Various vascular smooth muscle relaxants may favor the appearance of «Ca^{++} sparkles» under the smooth muscle sarcolemma. The Ca^{++} sparkles are thought to originate from local activation of the rynodine receptor immediately below the sarcolemma. These sparkles of Ca^{++} favor the relaxation by means:

A. Activation of Na^+-Ca^{++} antiport present in smooth muscle

B. Ca^{++} dependent calcineurin phosphatase activation in smooth muscle

C. Activation of K^+ channels dependent on Ca^{++} in smooth muscle

D. Activation of myosin light chain phosphorylase in smooth muscle

E. Activation of Rho kinase in smooth muscle

VIVA / SHORT QUESTION

Nerve and Neuromuscular Junction

1. What are the advantages of myelination?
   Ans: i) It increases the speed of conduction.
   ii) It reduces energy expenditure by the cell.
   iii) It provides a protective covering to the axon.
   iv) It is responsible for the colour of the white matter of the brain and spinal cord

2. What are the difference between myelinated and unmyelinated nerves?

Myelinated nerves	Unmyelinated nerves
1. Have axons of large diameter.	Have axons of small diameter.
2. Axons surrounded by concentric layers of Schwann cell plasma membrane	Axons surrounded by cytoplasm of Schwann cells.
3. Nerve impulse jumps from one node to the other node (saltatory conduction)	Nerve impulse travels uniformly along the axolemma.
4. Density of voltage gated Na^+ channels are more	Na^+ channels are less in axons
5. Saltatory conduction is fast and consumes less energy.	Conduction is slow and consumes more energy.
6. E.g.: All preganglionic fibers in ANS. In PNS, fibers more than 1µm in diameter.	All post-ganglionic fibers in ANS. In PNS, fibers less than 1µm in diameter.

3. What are the Neurotrophins?
   Ans: Neurotrophins are trophic proteins to the neurons, as they promote nerve growth and survival. They are produced by the nerves, muscles, glands and astrocytes. Some known neurotrophins are: Nerve growth factor, Brain-derived neurotrophic factor, Neurotrophin – 3, and Neurotrophin 4/5.

4. What are the types of neurons?
   Ans:
   i) Unipolar, Pseudounipolar, bipolar, multipolar (according to the number of processes)
   ii) Golgi Type 1, Golgi Type 2 (according to the length of the axon)
   iii) Sensory and motor neurons (according to functions)
   iv) Pyramidal cells and stellate cells (according to dendritic pattern)

5. Define electrotonic (or graded) potentials.
   Ans: Electrotonic potentials are local, non-propagated potentials of small magnitude, in response to a depolarizing or hyperpolarizing stimulus of lesser strength.

6. What are the properties of graded potentials?
   Ans: i) Graded in nature: The the magnitude of potential change is proportionate to the stimulus strength.
   ii) Decremental conduction: Graded potentials decay progressively with time and distance.
   iii) Depolarizing or hyperpolarizing nature
   v) Summation: if a second stimulus is applied before the potential produced by the first stimulus has disappeared, both the potential changes are added together producing a larger and/or prolonged wave in the recording.

7. What are the forms of graded potentials?
   Ans: End-plate potential, Receptor potential, Synaptic potential, Pacemaker potential.

8. Define threshold, suprathreshold, and subthreshold stimulus.
   Ans: Threshold stimulus: The strength of stimulus that brings the membrane potential *from –70 mV t~ -55 mV* is known as threshold stimulus.
   Suprathreshold stimulus: The stimulus higher in strength than the threshold stimulus.
   Subthreshold stimulus: The stimulus less in strength than the threshold stimulus.

9. What are rheobase, utilization time and chronaxie ?
   Ans: these are various components of strength-duration curve.
   Rheobase: To excite a tissue, the lowest strength of current required is termed as rheobase. Utilization time: The minimum time for which the rheobase must be applied to elicit an action potential.
   Chronaxie: It is the time required for a stimulus of double the rheobase strength to produce an action potential. The lesser the chronaxie, the greater is the excitability.

10. Define action potential.
    Ans: Action potential is defined as a transient change in membrane potential of about 100 mV, which is conducted along the axon in an all-or-none fashion.

11. What are the phases of action potential ?
    Ans: Two phases, a phase of depolarization and a phase of repolarization.
    i) Phase of depolarization consists of slow depolarization to threshold and a rapid rising phase.
    ii) Phase of repolarization includes a rapid falling phase, after-depolarization and after-hyperpolarization phase.

12. What are the ionic bases of the phases of action potential ?
    Ans: Depolarization is due to influx of sodium (by voltage-gated Na^+ channels) and repolarization is due to efflux of potassium (by voltage-gated K^+channels).

13. What is All- or- none law?
    Ans: All or none states that if an action potential is formed, it appears with its maximum size and shape, otherwise it does not form at all.

14. What is Absolute refractory period?
    Ans: Absolute refractory period is the period in the action potential during which, application of a second stimulus of any strength and duration does not produce another action potential. The ARP corresponds to the period from the time the firing level is reached until repolarization is about one-third complete.

15. What is the mechanism and importance of absolute refractory period?
Ans: Mechanism of ARP: During the absolute refractory period, the inactivation gates of the voltage-gated sodium channels close. These sodium channels can reopen only after some time when they attain the resting state. Hence, even if a stronger stimulus is applied, it does not produce a second action potential. Importance of ARP: ARP determines the rate of discharge of nerve fiber, and is responsible for the one-way conduction of action potentials.

16. What is the mechanism of relative refractory period?
Ans: During RRP, some of the channels have returned to their initial resting state, and they open in response to a second stimulus. Also, a suprathreshold stimulus spreads to larger area over the membrane and open more number of voltage-gated sodium channel.

17. What is relative refractory period?
Ans: Relative refractory period (RRP) is the period following ARP during which, application of only a suprathreshold stimulus can elicit a second action potential. The RRP starts from the end of ARP to the start of after-depolarization.

18. What are the properties of nerve fiber?
Ans: Excitability, Conductivity, Unfatigability, Refractory period, All or none law, Summation, Accommodation

19. Classify nerve fibers?
Ans: Three categories: A, B and C.
Type A: Diameter 12–20 µm , conduction velocity 70 to 120 m/sec
Aα fibers supply extrafusal fibers in skeletal muscles and also carry proprioception. Aβ fibers carry touch pressure sensation and act as motor fibers. Aγ fibers supply intrafusal fibers in muscle spindles. Aδ fibers are mainly fast conducting nociceptive fibers
Type B: Diameter < 3 µm , conduction velocity 3 to 15 m/sec Type C: Diameter 0.4 – 1.2 µm , conduction velocity 0.5 to 2 m/sec

20. What are the fetures of Wallerian degeneration?
Ans: The degenerative changes occur in the distal segment of the axon.
Synaptic transmission occurring at the axon terminal stops within hours. The axon swells and the terminals retract from the postsynaptic target, the axon and all its terminals degenerate. round fatty enlargements form all over the myelin sheath. The myelin sheath breaks down but the myelinating cells remain viable. The debris created by the disintegration of the axon and its myelin is devoured by macrophages

21. What are the degenerative changes occur in proximal segment?
Ans: These changes are known as retrograde degeneration. The cell body swells and become rounded.
The nucleus also swells and moves to an eccentric position. Endoplasmic reticulum reassembles around the periphery of the cell body. The ribosomes appear disorganized. The Nissl granules gradually disintegrate and are stained weakly with basic dyes; this is known as chromatolysis.

22. What are the regenerative changes folowing nerve injury?
Ans: The proximal end of the axon develops many sprouts. The sprouts elongate by formation of a growth cone at their growing ends. The Schwann cells that had survived the degeneration multiply and form rows along the pathway previously taken by the disintegrated distal axon. Out of the many sprouting branches, one branch finds the way through the Schwann cells and finally reinnervates the original target structure. Number of Nissl granules slowly reappears. Other organelles also reappear.
The cell loses excess fluid and regains its normal size. The nucleus occupies the central position

23. What are steps of neuromuscular transmission?
Ans: Arrival of an action potential at the axon terminal depolarizes the membrane. This leads to opening of the voltage-gated calcium channels, calcium influx and then calcium-mediated exocytosis of the synaptic vesicles containing Ach. Ach molecules diffuse across the synaptic cleft, bind to the receptors present at the post-synaptic membrane. This binding causes Na^+ influx, producing end plate potential.

24. Name some neuromuscular blockers.
Ans: Presynaptic blockers: Botulinum toxin, Hemicholinium
Postsynaptic blockers: Competitive blockers (Curare, Gallamine); Depolarizing blockers (Succinylcholine, Carbamylcholine), Reversible AchE inhibitors (Neostigmine and Physostigmine), Irreversible AchE inhibitors (pesticides like parathion, malathion and baygon)

25. What is myasthenia gravis?
Ans: Myasthenia gravis results from a decrease in the number of AChR present on the motor end plate due to production of circulating autoantibodies against these receptors. The patient presents with fatigue, muscle weakness, drooping of eyelids and decremental response to repetitive nerve stimulation on EMG. Treated with AChE inhibitors such as pyridostigmine, neostigmine, Immunosuppression, Plasmapheresis and Thymectomy.

Muscle Physiology

26. What are the skeletal muscle proteins?
Ans: Contractile proteins: myosin and actin; Regulatory proteins: troponin and tropomyosin; Attachment proteins: titin, nebulin, alpha actinin, desmin, myomesin and dystrophin.

27. What are the differences between isometric and isotonic contractions?

Ans:	Isometric	isotonic
Length of muscle	Remains same	Shortening occurs
Tension	Tension increases	No change
External work	No work done	Work is done

28. What are the properties of skeletal muscles?
Ans: Summation of contraction, Staircase Phenomenon, Tetanization, Post-tetanic potentiation, Length-tension relationship, Load-velocity relationship

29. What is summation of contraction?

Ans: When the second stimulus is applied before relaxation has occurred, the contractile responses are added to produce a higher response. The Ca^{2+} released due to the second stimulus is added to the Ca^{2+} released due to the first stimulus, producing a higher sarcoplasmic Ca^{2+} concentration that results in a bigger contractile response.

30. What is staircase Phenomenon?

Ans: If a skeletal muscle is stimulated rapidly, but below the tetanizing frequency, there is progressive increase in the force of contraction for the first few contractions. This is the staircase phenomenon or treppe. This is because the leftover calcium from the first contraction is added to the calcium released during the second contraction and results in greater amplitude. Also, the heat produced during preceding contraction decreases sarcoplasmic viscosity and facilitates the enzymatic activity that increases the height of succeeding contractions.

31. What is critical frequency (CF)?

Ans: When a muscle is stimulated with a frequency more than CF, summation of contractions occurs. Stimulation of the muscle with less than CF produces distinct contractions with intermittent relaxations. CF = 1/ Twitch duration (in sec). A fast muscle needs a larger CF and a slow muscle needs a smaller CF.

32. What is length-tension relationship?

Ans: Within physiological limit, the tension is directly proportional to the initial length of the muscle.

33. What is resting length?

Ans: The length at which there is optimum overlap between actin and myosin filaments that can lead to maximum tension development. The optimal sarcomeric length in frog muscle is 2.0–2.2 μm.

34. What is Passive tension, Total tension and Active tension?

Ans: Passive tension: When the muscle fiber is stretched, the tension registered by it is known as the passive tension, which is due to the elongation of the elastic titin filaments, not due to activation of the contractile elements.

Total tension: When the stretched muscle is stimulated, the tension developed by it is known as the total tension.

Active tension: At any length, the amount of tension actually generated by the cross bridge movements is known as the active tension, which is the difference between the total tension minus passive tension.

35. What is oxygen debt?

Ans: The amount of extra oxygen taken up by the body above the basal O_2 consumption following exercise is known as oxygen debt. After the exercise is over, body has to convert the surplus lactate into pyruvate, replenish the ATP and Creatine phosphate stores in the muscle, to replaced the O_2 that came from myoglobin. For all the above functions, O_2 is required.

36. What is Rigor Mortis?

Ans: It is the stiffness in the muscle that starts about 3 to 4 h after death and gets completed in about 12 h after death. Following death, the cytoplasmic calcium concentration remains elevated because calcium is not pumped back into the sarcoplasmic reticulum in the absence of ATP. Also, Ca^{2+} diffuses from ECF into the cytoplasm and Ca^{2+} diffuses out of SR to the sarcoplasm, as the inactive membrane of the SR cannot hold back Ca^{2+}. The raised cytoplasmic calcium concentration initiates contraction.

37. What are the differences between type I and II muscle fibers

Ans:	**Type I**	**Type II**
1. Other names	Slow; red; oxidative	Fast; white; glycolytic
2. Contraction velocity	Slow	Fast
3. Myosin ATPase	Low	High
4. Ca^{2+}-pumping capacity of SR	Low	High
5. Rate of fatigue	Slow	Fast
6. Fiber diameter	Moderate	Large
7. Size of motor unit	Small	Large
8. Glycogen content	Low	High
9. Glycolytic capacity	Low	High
10. Oxidative capacity	High	Low
11. Mitochondria	Numerous	Less
12. Myoglobin content	High	Low
13. Capillaries	Many	Few
14. Primary source of ATP production	Oxidative phosphorylation	Glycolysis

38. What are the properties of smooth muscle?

Ans: A. Morphological properties (Lack of striations, Absence of Troponin, Absence of T-tubules, Absence of well-developed neuromuscular junctions)

B. Electrical properties (Presence of gap junctions, Excitability, Variable RMP and shifting pacemakers, Variable action potentials)

C. Mechanical properties (Tonus, Plasticity, Slow and prolonged contractile response, Length-tension relationship, Force-velocity relationship, Muscle hypertrophy)

39. What is latch-bridge mechanism?

Ans: When MLCP-induced dephosphorylation of myosin light-chain takes place, it does not bring about dissociation of myosin from actin until the cytoplasmic calcium concentration falls below a critical level. This attached cross-bridges following dephosphorylation are known as the latch-bridges.

40. What is plasticity of smooth muscle?

Ans: The length-tension relationship is variable in smooth muscles. When a smooth muscle is stretched, it initially shortens and exerts tension. However, if the stretch is maintained, gradually the tension decreases and if the stretch is increased, the tension may not rise proportionately or at a particular length, the tension may increase considerably. The adaptability of the smooth muscle to the new length with less increase in tension is known as plasticity.

SECTION IV - AUTONOMIC NERVOUS SYSTEM

MULTIPLE CHOICE QUESTIONS

1. A 54-year-old man is admitted to hospital to undergo an operation. In the anaesthetic room he becomes very anxious and upset. He becomes cold and sweaty and on closer examination you notice his body hair is erect and his pupils are widely dilated. His heart rate increases and he is combative. The anaesthetist has to call for help and the operation is cancelled. Which part of the nervous system is responsible for the changes seen in this patient?
   A. Enteric nervous system
   B. Sympathetic nervous system
   C. Parasympathetic nervous system
   D. Corticospinal tract
   E. Spinothalamic tract

2. Which of the following receptors is found in the sympathetic and parasympathetic nodes?
   A. Nicotinic
   B.Muscarinic
   C. Beta1-adrenergic
   D. Alpha1-adrenergic
   E. None of the above

3. Indicate if any of the following is the neurotransmitter used in the transmission of the ganglia of the parasympathetic vegetative system
   A. Serotonin
   B. Noradrenaline
   C. Adrenaline
   D. GABA
   E. None of them

4. In which of the following nerve cells are nicotinic receptors found?
   A. Sympathetic effector cells
   B. Sympathetic ganglion cells
   C. Parasympathetic effector cells
   D. Intrinsic Interneurons of the sympathetic ganglion
   E. In none of the above

5. The peripheral nervous system consists of the somatic and autonomic systems. The autonomic nervous system is subdivided into the parasympathetic (cholinergic) and sympathetic (adrenergic) systems. Which statement about the sympathetic nervous system is true?
   A. The pre-ganglionic fibres emerge from the cervical and thoracic segments of the spinal cord
   B. Most of the sympathetic ganglia lie outside the sympathetic chain
   C. Some pre-ganglionic fibres synapse at the adrenal cortex
   D. Some post-ganglionic fibres synapse at the adrenal medulla
   E. The male genital tract receives sympathetic supply via the pelvic ganglion

6. This neurotransmitter is present in all synapses between the preganglionic and postganglionic fibers and between parasympathetic postganglionic terminations and effector organs. What neurotransmitter is it?
   A. Acetylcholine
   B. GABA
   C. Renin
   D. Dopamine
   E. Secretin

VIVA / SHORT QUESTION

1. What are the functions of ANS?

Ans: i) Maintenance of homeostatic conditions of the body.
ii) Regulation of visceral activities, such as GIT, Heart etc.
iii) Smoothening body's responses to environmental changes.
iv) Coordination of body's responses to exercise and stress.
v) Assisting the endocrine system to regulate reproductive functions.

2. What are the divisions of ANS?

Ans: i) Sympathetic system (Thoracolumbar division)
ii) Parasympathetic system (Craniosacral division)
iii) Enteric nervous system (Third division of ANS)

3. What are the cholinergic neurons?

Ans: Acetylcholine is the neurotransmitter at the following nerve terminals (**cholinergic fibers**) in ANS:
i) Preganglionic nerve terminals of both the sympathetic and the parasympathetic divisions.
ii) All parasympathetic postganglionic neurons.
iii) Postganglionic sympathetic neurons to sweat glands and blood vessels in skeletal muscle.

4. How do the preganglionic neurons differ between sympathetic and parasympathetic system?

Preganglionic neurons	Sympathetic	Parasympathetic
i) originate from	Intermediolateral horn of thoracolumbar segments of spinal cord	Cranial nerve nuclei in brainstem, & intermediolateral horn of sacral segments of spinal cord
ii) compared to postganglionic neurons	are shorter	are much longer
iii) terminate in	sympathetic chain of ganglia	the ganglion which is located near the viscera or in the viscera

5. How do the post-ganglionic neurons differ between sympathetic and parasympathetic system?

Postganglionic neurons	Sympathetic	Parasympathetic
i) originate from	sympathetic chain of ganglia	the ganglion which is located near the viscera or in the viscera
ii) compared to preganglionic neurons	are much longer	are shorter
iii) terminate	in the viscera	in the viscera

6. What are the types of sympathetic ganglia?

Ans: Sympathetic ganglia are of three types: paravertebral, prevertebral and terminal
i) Paravertebral:
a) cervical ganglia: superior, middle and inferior;
b) 12 thoracic ganglia ($T_1 - T_{12}$);
c) 5 lumbar ganglia;
d) 4 to 5 sacral ganglia
ii) Prevertebral:
a) Celiac: The preganglionic axons originate in the T^5 to T^{12} spinal levels and provide innervation to the stomach, small intestine, liver, pancreas, gallbladder, spleen & kidneys.
b) superior mesenteric: The preganglionic fibers originate in T^{10} to T^{12} and innervate the small & large intestines
c) Inferior mesenteric: The preganglionic fibers originate from L1 to L3 and innervate the lower part of colon, rectum, urinary bladder & reproductive organs.
iii) Terminal: These are located in the organ innervated by sympathetic fibers. Examples are adrenal medulla, heart, pancreas and urinary bladder

7. What are the types of sympathetic ganglia?

Ans: The fight-or-flight response is a typical widespread response of sympathetic activation. This occurs in critical situations of life when one has to either fight the situation or flee from the situation. The secretion of catecholamine from adrenal medulla contributes considerably. There is increase in: BP, breathing, salivary secretion, glucose and fatty acid level, sweating, cutaneous vasoconstriction, piloerection, pupillary dilation alertness, and decreased activity of bowel and bladder.

8. What are the functions of parasympathetic system?

Ans: Parasympathetic system restores body's energy reserve. They reduce HR, and stimulate intestinal motility, secretion, digestion and absorption, and promote reproductive functions.

9. What is Argyll Robertson Pupil?

Ans: Accommodation reflex present (arp), but light reflex is absent. It is a disorder in a patient of neurosyphilis due to lesion of pretectal nucleus of midbrain which is one of the cell stations in light reflex pathway.

10. What is Horner's Syndrome?

Ans: This is a syndrome of autonomic dysfunction, characterized by:
i) Presence of ptosis (drooping of the upper eyelid)
ii) Miosis (constriction of pupil)
iii) Facial anhidrosis (lack of sweating on the affected side of face and neck).

SECTION V- CARDIOVASCULAR SYSTEM

MULTIPLE CHOICE QUESTIONS

1. The lungs provide oxygen to and remove carbon dioxide from the blood. Which of the following parts of the cardiovascular system contains well-oxygenated blood in a normal adult?
   A. Pulmonary arteries
   B. Pulmonary veins
   C. Inferior vena cava
   D. Right atrium
   E. Right ventricle

2. Cardiac myocytes (cardiac muscle cells) are like skeletal muscle, but differ owing to its different function. Which of the following statements about cardiac muscle is true?
   A. Striations are absent
   B. The muscle fibres do not branch
   C. Low resistance bridges exist to allow impulses to travel from one cardiac fibre to another
   D. Contains actin, myosin, and tropomyosin, but no troponin
   E. Over 25% of the energy is derived from anaerobic respiration

3. A balloon catheter is inserted from the superior vena cava into the heart and inflated to increase the pressure in the atrium by 10 mmHg. Which of the following groups of physiological changes should be expected in response to elevated atrial pressure? Renal sympathetic nerve activity Atrial natriuretic peptide Sodium excretion Option 1 ↑ ↑ ↑ Option 2 ↑ ↓ ↑ Option 3 ↑ ↓ ↓ Option 4 ↑ ↑ ↓ Option 5 ↓ ↓ ↓ Option 6 ↓ ↑ ↓ Option 7 ↓ ↑ ↑ Option 8 ↓ ↓ ↑
   A. Option 1 B. Option 3 C. Option 5
   D. Option 7 E. Option 8 F. Option 6
   G. Option 7 H. Option 8

4. The myogenic mechanism of self-regulation of vascular smooth muscle tone:
   A. Requires release of nitric oxide by endothelial cells
   B. Involves the release of noradrenaline from sympathetic nerve endings
   C. Responds to changes in transmural pressure of the vessel wall
   D. Depends on changes in flow through the vessel
   E. Originates from changes in shear stress in the vascular wall

5. The sinoatrial (SA) node is known as the cardiac pacemaker. Of the following statements about the conduction of impulses from the SA node to the ventricles, which is true?
   A. The time taken is represented by the QRS complex on the ECG
   B. It is increased by adenosine
   C. Stimulation of the vagus nerve increases the rate of conduction
   D. Increased rate of conduction may result in supraventricular tachycardia
   E. Complete interruption of the conduction results in first-degree heart block

6. In the heart, the impulse from the sinus node passes from the atria into the ventricles through the A-V bundle, also known as the bundle of His. Which of the following causes does NOT lead to blockage of this impulse?
   A. Ischaemia of the A-V bundle
   B. Compression of the A-V bundle
   C. Inflammation of the A-V bundle
   D. Extreme stimulation of the heart by the vagus nerves
   E. Patent foramen ovale

7. If the S-A node discharges at 0.00 s, when will the action potential normally reach the ventricular septum?
   A. 0.22 sec **B. 0.16 sec** C. 0.12 sec
   D. 0.09 sec E. 0.03 sec

8. If the S-A node discharges at 0.00 s, when will the action potential normally reach the A-V beam?
   A. 0.80 sec B. 0.16 sec **C. 0.12 sec**
   D. 0.09 sec E. 0.03 sec

9. A 55-year-old man attends the emergency department with acute chest pain. He is diagnosed with inferior myocardial infarction.Which leads on the ECG will show ST elevation?
   A. II, III, aVF B. V5–V6 C. I, aVL, V6
   D. V4R E. V1–2

10. A 60-year-old woman presented to A&E with dyspnoea, fatigue and palpitations. Vital signs were recorded as pulse 120 bpm, RR 25, SaO2 97% on air, BP 140/80 mmHg. Her ECG is shown below. What is the most likely diagnosis from the list below?

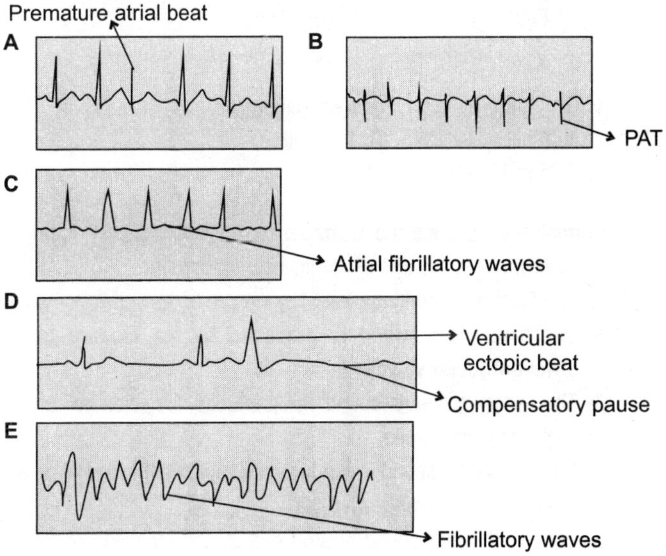

A. Complete heart block
B. Left bundle branch block (LBBB)
C. Sinus bradycardia
D. Atrial fibrillation
E. Right bundle branch block (RBBB)

11. Normal heart sounds are produced by the opening and closing of valves during the cardiac cycle. Which of the following describes the first heart sound?
A. It is caused by the closure of AV valve
B. It is partly caused by the closure of the pulmonary valve
C. It is louder at the base than the apex of the heart
D. It signals the end of ventricular systole
E. It has a higher pitch than the second heart sound

12. A 70-year-old woman had an electrocardiogram at her annual checkup and the following tracing was obtained at lead II. According to Einthoven's law, if the voltage of the QRS in its lead III is - 0.5 mV, what is the voltage of the QRS in lead I?

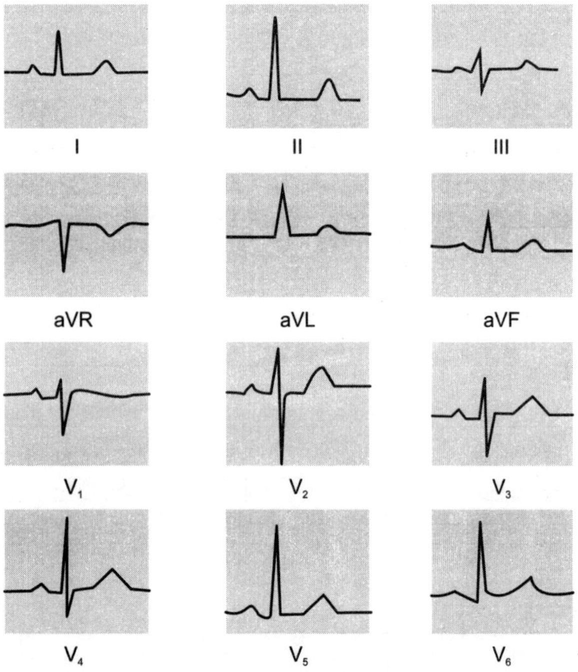

A. 0.05 millivolts
B. 0.50 millivolts
C. 1.05 millivolts
D. 1.25 millivolts
E. 2.05 millivolts

13. Normal heart sounds are produced by the opening and closing of heart valves. What is true of normal heart sounds?
A. The first heart sound is caused by closure of the semilunar valves
B. The first heart sound is produced by the closure of the atrioventricular valves
C. The second heart sound is produced by closure of the atrioventricular valves
D. The third heart sound is produced by rapid ventricular filling and opening of the semilunar valves
E. The fourth heart sound is produced by the emptying of the left ventricle into the aorta

14. Which of the following heart murmurs are heard during systole? Which of the following heart murmurs are heard during systole?
A. Aortic valve insufficiency
B. Pulmonary valve insufficiency
C. Tricuspid valve stenosis
D. Mitral valve stenosis
E. Patent ductus arteriosus

15. Factors that affect stroke volume and heart rate affect cardiac output. Which of the following options increases cardiac output in a normal heart?
A. A decrease in heart rate
B. A decrease in stroke volume
C. Stimulation of the sympathetic nervous system
D. Decrease in end-diastolic volume
E. moderate changes in environmental temperature

16. Which of the following factors normally causes the cardiac output curve to shift right following the pressure axis in the right atrium?
A. Intrapleural pressure drop to 6 mmHg
B. Increased systemic medium fill pressure
C. Withdrawal of ventilator and use of normal breathing
D. Surgical opening of the chest
E. Breathing against negative pressure

17. A patient comes in for an annual check-up in apparently good health. However, she is concerned about her heart because of her family history. You perform a cardiovascular function examination. Her blood pressure is 128/83 mmHg, and the echocardiography indicates that the telediastolic volume is 140 mL and the telesystolic volume is 80 mL. A usual ECG is performed, as shown below. Heart rate is 79 beats/min. You estimate that this patient's cardiac output is:
A. 4,4 L/min
B. 4,7 L/min
C. 5,2 L/min
D. 5,5 L/min
E. 6,3 L/min.

18. Which of the following is normally associated with increased cardiac output?
A. Cardiac tamponade
B. Increased venous distensibility
C. Moderate anemia
D. Severe aortic stenosis
E. Surgical opening of the chest

19. A 40-year-old woman is hospitalized and has severe anemia. The patient has a cardiac output of 12.5 L/min, an oxygen consumption of 250 mL/min and a pulmonary artery oxygen concentration of 160 mL/L of blood. What is the oxygen concentration in the pulmonary vein, in units of mL/L of blood?
A. 140
B. 150
C. 160
D. 180
E. 200

20. A 22-year-old student is physically examined to certify that he can participate in athletic testing. During the cardiovascular scan you detect that your heart rate is 60 beats/min and blood pressure is 118/68 mmHg. In echocardiography the end-diastolic volume is 150 mL and the end-systolic volume is 60 mL. Cardiac output is:
A. 4.5 L/min
B. 5 L/min
C. 5.4 L/min
D. 5.9 L/min
E. 6.3 L/min

21. A 24-year-old man consults for a systematic physical examination. His blood pressure AT REST is currently 120/80 mmHg and his heart rate is 75 beats/min. He is recommended to begin an exercise program. When he returns 3 months later his heart rate has decreased to 50 beats/min (asymptomatic). What values would you expect to see in this patient AT REST compared to those obtained 3 months earlier?
A. Increased differential pressure and unchanged cardiac output
B. Increased differential pressure and increased cardiac output
C. Decreased differential pressure and increased cardiac output
D. Decreased differential pressure and unchanged cardiac output
E. Increased differential pressure and decreased cardiac output

22. **With a cardiac output curve defined by the red line and a venous return curve defined by the blue line (balanced at a point)**, what is the resistance to venous return in units of mmHg/L/min?

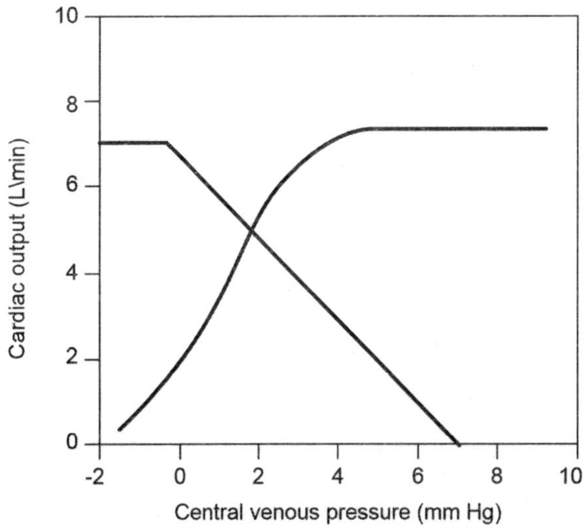

A. 1,70 B. 1,40 C. 1,23
D. 0,65 E. 0,35

23. A 63-year-old man was admitted to the hospital 1 hour after having substernal chest pain. He was weak and sweaty and his heart was beating rapidly at 90 beats/min as a result of having a coronary artery occlusion that reduced blood flow to the left ventricle. In the ECG, it was determined that the tachycardia originated in the SA node. Before treatment could be started, the weakness was increasing and the arterial pulse increased to approximately 45 beats/min, although the ECG showed an atrial rate of 90 beats/min. A cardiac pacemaker was inserted as the AV node had been damaged by ischemia. With the pacemaker implanted and adjusted to 75 beats/min the patient felt somewhat better, and pharmacological treatment was initiated.The mechanism most likely responsible for the reduction of the patient's arterial pulse to approximately 40 beats/min after impulse conduction through the AV junction is:
A. Excitation of the ventricles through an AV bypass pathway
B. Conversion of ventricular myocardial fibers into automatic cells
C. Discharge of ectopic ventricular cells that have the same electrophysiological characteristics as SA node cells
D. Discharge of automatic cells (Purkinje fibers) into the specialized conduction system of the ventricles
E. Excitation of ventricular cells by rhythmic activity in the autonomic neurons that innervate the heart

24. A 50-year-old woman has a renal blood flow of 1000 mL/min and a hematocrit of 50. Her blood pressure is 120 mmHg and her renal venous pressure is 20 mmHg. She has a plasma colloidosmotic pressure of 25 mmHg. Which of the following is her total renal vascular resistance (in mmHg/mL/min)?
A. 0.10 B. 0.20 C. 0.50
D. 1.00 E. 1.50

25. 2.A healthy 30-year-old man rises from a supine position. Which of the following groups of cardiovascular modifications is most likely to have occurred? Total peripheral resistanceHeart rateSympathetic nerve activityOption 1↑↑↑Option 2↑↓↑Option 3↑↓↓Option 4↑↑↓Option 5↓↓↓Option 6↓↑↓Option 7↓↑↑Option 8↓↓↑
A. Option 1 B. Option 2
C. Option 3 D. Option 4
E. Option 5 F. Option 6
G. Option 7 H. Option 8

26. The diameter of a precapillary arteriole increases in a muscular vascular bed. For which of the following factors would a decrease be expected?
A. Capillary filtration rate
B. Vascular conductance
C. Capillary blood flow
D. Hydrostatic capillary pressure
E. Resistance of the arteriole

27. A 78-year-old woman has an average blood pressure of 120 mmHg and a heart rate of 60 bpm. She has a systolic volume of 50 ml, cardiac output of 3000 mL/min and a right atrial pressure of 0 mmHg. What is the total peripheral resistance (in mmHg/mL/min) in this woman?
A. 0.01
B. 0.02
C. 0.04
D. 0.08
E. 0.10

28. If the blood flow through the kidney is 1200 mL/min and the renal artery pressure is 100 mmHg, and the renal venous pressure is 0 mmHg, what is the conductance (in mL/min/mmHg) of the renal vessel?
   A. 2
   B. 4
   C. 8
   D. 12
   E. 16

29. A well-trained athlete has prepared himself to run the Boston Marathon. Our aim is to study how his cardiovascular system adapts to the high demands of the race. The heart rate (60 beats/min), blood pressure (110/80 mmHg) and cardiac output (4.2 L/min) are measured immediately before the athlete runs. Assume the central venous pressure is 0 mmHg and calculate the athlete's peripheral resistance.
   A. 42.8 mmHg/L/min
   B. 32.1 mmHg/L/min
   C. 21.4 mmHg/L/min
   D. 10.7 mmHg/L/min
   E. 4.3 mmHg/L/min

30. Most venous blood flow leaves the heart muscle through:
   A. Anterior heart veins
   B. Azygos vein C. Bronchial veins
   D. Coronary sinus E. Thebesian veins

31. Which of the following situations is normally associated with an increase in systemic medium fill pressure?
   A. Decreased blood volume and hypotension
   B. Increased venous distensibility
   C. Increased arterial distensibility
   D. **Left sided heart failure**
   E. Hypothyroidism

32. As the blood flows through the systemic circulation, its mean pressure varies. What is the normal range of pressure in capillaries from the arteriolar ends to the venous ends respectively?
   A. 55 mmHg to 35 mmHg
   B. 35 mmHg to 10 mmHg
   C. 55 mmHg to 10 mmHg
   D. 40 mmHg to 20 mmHg
   E. 40 mmHg to 10 mmHg

33. The mean arterial pressure is the average of the systolic and diastolic pressures in the arteries. As the blood flows through the systemic circulation, its mean pressure varies. In a healthy individual, what is the mean arterial pressure in the pulmonary arteries?
   A. 7 mmHg
   B. 8 mmHg
   C. 16 mmHg
   D. 20 mmHg
   E. 25 mmHg

34. Which of the following groups of physiological changes would you expect in a person rising from a supine position? Hydrostatic venous pressure in the legsParasympathetic nerve activityRenal blood flowOption 1↑↑↑Option 2↑↑↓Option 3↑↓↓Option 4↓↓↓Option 5↓↓↑Option 6↓↑↑
   A. Option 1 B. Option 2 **C. Option 3**
   D. Option 4 E. Option 5 F. Option 6

35. Using the following data, calculate the rate of net fluid movement (in mL/min) through the capillary wall. Plasma colloid osmotic pressure = 40 mmHg Capillary hydrostatic pressure = 10 mmHg Venous hydrostatic pressure = 5 mmHg Arterial pressure = 80 mmHg Interstitial hydrostatic pressure = 5 mmHg Interstitial colloid osmotic pressure = 5 mmHg
   A. 100 (filtration) B. 200 (reabsorption)
   C. 200 (filtration) D. 300 (filtration)
   E. 300 (reabsorption)

36. A 65-year-old male suffers from congestive heart failure. He has a heart rate of 4.0 L/min, a blood pressure of 115/85 and a heart rate of 90 bpm. Other tests performed by the cardiologist showed that the patient has a right atrial pressure of 10 mmHg. In this patient we would expect an increase in one or more of the factors shown below. Indicate which.
   A. Plasma colloidosmotic pressure
   B. Interstitial colloidosmotic pressure
   C. Blood pressure
   D. Cardiac output
   E. Hydrostatic pressure in the vena cava

37. A 56-year-old woman has congestive heart failure with generalized edema.Which of the following phenomena is very important for the formation of this woman's edema?
   A. Increased hydrostatic interstitial pressure
   B. Decreased interstitial oncotic pressure
   C. Increased plasma oncotic pressure
   D. Decreased renal excretion of Na+
   E. Decreased venous pressure

38. A suture is placed around the carotid artery and pulled to partially contract the vessel. Which of the following groups of physiological changes would most likely result from carotid artery contraction? Vagal toneHeart rateVenous distentionOption 1↑↑↑Option 2↑↑↓Option 3↑↓↓Option 4↑↓↑Option 5↓↓↓Option 6↓↓↑Option 7↓↑↑Option 8↓↑↓
   A. Option 1 B. Option 3 C. Option 5
   D. Option 7 E. Option 8 F. Option 6
   G. Option 7 H. Option 8

39. A 35-year-old woman goes to her family doctor for a check-up. She has an average blood pressure of 105 mmHg and a heart rate of 74 bpm. Other tests performed by a cardiologist showed that the patient had moderate aortic insufficiency. Which of the following groups of changes could be expected in this patient? Pulse pressure Stroke volume Systolic pressure Option 1 ↑↑↑ Option 2 ↑↓↑ Option

3 ↑ ↓ ↓ Option 4 ↑ ↑ ↓ Option 5 ↓ ↓ ↓ Option 6 ↓ ↑ ↓ Option 7 ↓ ↑ ↑ Option 8 ↓ ↓ ↓

A. Option 1 **B. Option 2** C. Option 3
D. Option 4 E. Option 5 F. Option 6
G. Option 7 H. Option 8

40. A 65-year-old woman goes to her family doctor for a check-up. She has an average blood pressure of 95 mmHg and a heart rate of 74 bpm. Other tests performed by a cardiologist showed that the patient had moderate aortic insufficiency. Which of the following groups of changes could be expected in this patient? Pulse pressure Stroke volume Systolic pressure Option 1 ↑ ↑ ↑ Option 2 ↑ ↓ ↑ Option 3 ↑ ↓ ↓ Option 4 ↑ ↑ ↓ Option 5 ↓ ↓ ↓ Option 6 ↓ ↑ ↓ Option 7 ↓ ↑ ↑ Option 8 ↓ ↓ ↑
    A. Option 1 **B. Option 2** C. Option 3
    D. Option 4 E. Option 5

41. A well-trained athlete has prepared himself to run the Boston Marathon. Our aim is to study how his cardiovascular system adapts to the high demands of the race. The heart rate (60 beats/min), blood pressure (110/80 mmHg) and cardiac output (4.2 L/min) are measured immediately before the athlete runs. What is this athlete's differential pressure?
    A. 100 mmHg B. 90 mmHg C. 80 mmHg
    D. 60 mmHg **E. 30 mmHg**

42. A 22-year-old student is physically examined to certify that he can participate in athletic testing. During the cardiovascular scan you detect that your heart rate is 60 beats/min and blood pressure is 118/68 mmHg. In echocardiography the end-diastolic volume is 150 mL and the end-systolic volume is 60 mL.From these data you estimate that the differential pressure is:
    A. 50 mmHg B. 60 mmHg C. 68 mmHg
    D. 80 mmHg E. 90 mmHg

43. A 22-year-old student is physically examined to certify that he can participate in athletic testing. During the cardiovascular scan you detect that your heart rate is 60 beats/min and blood pressure is 118/68 mmHg. In echocardiography the end-diastolic volume is 150 mL and the end-systolic volume is 60 mL. It is estimated that the patient's mean blood pressure is:
    A. 68 mmHg B.77 mm Hg
    C. 84 mmHg 92 mmHg
    E. 118 mmHg

44. Which of the following statements is true?
    A. Natriuretic peptides are powerful vasoconstrictors
    B. Stimulation of angiotensin II receptors produces vasoconstriction
    C. Eccentric ventricular hypertrophy is typical of valve regurgitation and is due to the synthesis of new myofibrils arranged in parallel
    D. Parietal pressure is one of the main determinants of oxygen consumption by the heart
    E. As predicted by Laplace's law, as the ventricular radius increases, parietal tension and therefore oxygen consumption will decrease

45. Which of the following would occur as a result of increased atrial pressure?
    A. Decreased plasma Atrial natriuretic peptide (ANP)
    B. Increased plasma concentration of angiotensin II
    C. Increased plasma concentration of aldosterone and cortisol
    D. Increased renal sodium excretion
    E. Increased systemic arterial pressure

46. A 63-year-old man was admitted to the hospital 1 hour after having substernal chest pain. He was weak and sweaty and his heart was beating rapidly at 90 beats/min as a result of having a coronary artery occlusion that reduced blood flow to the left ventricle. In the ECG, it was determined that the tachycardia originated in the SA node. Before treatment could be started, the weakness increased and the arterial pulse rose to approximately 45 beats/min, although the ECG showed an atrial rate of 90 beats/min. A cardiac pacemaker was inserted as the AV node had been damaged by ischemia. With the pacemaker implanted and adjusted to 75 beats/min the patient felt somewhat better, and pharmacological treatment was initiated. Shortly after coronary artery occlusion the [K+] interstitial fluid increased greatly in the private flow region. In this region the high extracellular [K+]:
    A. Increased the speed of propagation of myocardial action potentials increased
    B. Reduced refractoriness after myocardial cell repolarization
    C. Depolarized the transmembrane potential at rest to a less negative value
    D. Reduced myocardial cell automatism
    E. Reduced the likelihood of re-entry arrhythmias

47. Obstruction of a coronary artery leads to death and necrosis of the muscle. Which of the following changes may occur within 24–48 hours of acute, complete obstruction of the right coronary artery?
    A. Cyanosis and oedema of the right ventricle
    B. Increased red cell count
    C. ST elevation in leads II, III, and aVL in the ECG D. Q waves in leads II, III, and aV in the ECG
    E. Development of granulation tissue in the right ventricle

48. As a consequence of which of the following groups of changes in a microcirculatory bed would the decrease in the diameter of an arteriole be more likely? Interstitial hydrostatic pressure Capillary hydrostatic pressure Lymphatic flow Option 1 ↑ ↑ ↑ Option 2 ↑ ↑ ↓ Option 3 ↑ ↓ ↓ Option 4 ↓ ↓ ↓ Option 5 ↓ ↓ ↑ Option 6 ↓ ↑ ↑
    A. Option 1 B. Option 2 C. Option 3
    D. Option 4 E. Option 5 F. Option 6

49. 4.A 63-year-old man was admitted to the hospital 1 hour after having substernal chest pain. He was weak and sweaty and his heart was beating rapidly at 90 beats/min as a result of having a coronary artery occlusion that reduced blood flow to the left ventricle. In the ECG, it was determined that the tachycardia originated in the SA node. Before treatment could be started, the weakness increased and the arterial pulse rose to approximately 45 beats/min, although the ECG showed an atrial rate of 90 beats/min. A cardiac pacemaker was inserted as

the AV node had been damaged by ischemia. With the pacemaker implanted and adjusted to 75 beats/min the patient felt somewhat better, and pharmacological treatment was initiated.The mechanism by which the SA node generated impulses at a rapid frequency during the early stages of coronary artery occlusion involves an increase in:

A. The slope of ascent of the action potential (phase 0) of the automatic cells

B. The slope of the slow diastolic depolarization of the automatic cells

C. The discharge threshold (less negative potential) of automatic cells

D. The negativity (hyperpolarization) of the initial portion of the slow diastolic depolarization

E. The amplitude of the action potential of automatic cells

50. Which of the following groups of physiological changes would you expect in a person rising from a supine position? Sympathetic nerve activityHeart rateTotal peripheral resistanceOption 1↑↑↑Option 2↑↑↓Option 3↑↓↓Option 4↑↓↑Option 5↓↓↓Option 6↓↓↑Option 7↓↑↑Option 8↓↑↓

A. Option 1

B. Option 2

C. Option 3

D. Option 4

E. Option 5

F. Option 6

G. Option 7

H. Option 8

51. A 60-year-old man visits his family doctor for his annual check-up. He has a blood pressure of 180/100 mmHg, a heart rate of 78 bpm and a pulse pressure of 80 mmHg. His plasma cholesterol concentration is in the upper 25th percentile. In which of the following factors does a decrease offer the most likely explanation of this patient's high pulse pressure?

A. Systolic volume

B. Blood pressure

C. Heart rate

D. Arterial distensibility

E. Total peripheral resistance

52. A 22-year-old male is admitted to the hospital emergency department after severing a major artery during a motorcycle accident. It is estimated that he has lost approximately 700 mL of blood. His blood pressure is 90/55 mm Hg. For which of the following factors would you expect a decrease as a result of bleeding?

A. Heart rate

B. Sympathetic nerve activity

C. Total peripheral resistance

D. Plasma renin activity

E. **Number of impulses from the carotid sinus**

53. A patient presents to the emergency department in extremis. Examination reveals elevated JVP, muffled heart sounds and worsening hypotension. Which of the following best describes the type of circulatory shock?

A. Obstructive shock

B. Hypovolaemic shock

C. Cardiogenic shock

D. Distributive shock

E. Anaphylactic shock

54. Cardiac (heart) failure occurs when the heart is unable to maintain the necessary cardiac output. Which of the following statements would you associate with cardiac failure?

A. Cardiac failure cannot occur if the cardiac output is over 5 litres per minute

B. Cardiac failure may be compensated for in the early stages by increased ventricular end-diastolic volume.

C. Cardiac failure may be precipitated by polycythaemia vera

D. Cardiac failure may be associated with a decrease in cardiac output with exercise

E. Cardiac failure often results in ventricular atrophy

55. Heart failure occurs when the heart is unable to maintain necessary cardiac output despite normal venous pressures. Which of the following events occurs in congestive cardiac failure?

A. The parasympathetic nervous system is stimulated

B. Aldosterone secretion is reduced

C. Reabsorption of sodium in renal tubules is reduced

D. Glomerular filtration rate is increased

E. Total body sodium is increased

56. Blood is drawn from a 56-year-old male with a 5-year history of congestive heart failure. There are high plasma concentrations of angiotensin II, aldosterone and atrial natriuretic peptide. The increase in which of the following factors is the most likely explanation for the increase in plasma concentrations of the atrial natriuretic peptide?

A. Blood pressure

B. Renal vascular resistance

C. Venous hydrostatic pressure

D. Pressure in the atrium

E. Cardiac output

VIVA / SHORT QUESTION

1. What is Windkessel effect?
Ans: The aorta and large arteries have more elastic elements in their wall. During systole, their wall stretches to accommodate the blood ejected by ventricles, and during diastole, their wall recoils back to presystolic position. This recoiling effect is called Windkessel effect.

2. What are the differences between systemic and the pulmonary circulation?
Ans:

	Systemic Circulation	Pulmonary Circulation
1. Pressures	High pressure	Low pressure
2. Arteries & Arterioles	Thick wall and narrow lumen	Thin wall and large lumen
3. Capillaries	Long and narrow	Short and wide
4. Resting Sympathetic tone)	High vasoconstrictor tone at rest)	Absent (lack vasoconstrictor tone
5. Peripheral resistance	High	Low
6. Capillary	Continuous	Pulsatile
7. Synonyms	Peripheral or greater circulation	Central or lesser circulation

3. What is intrinsic heart rate?
Ans: When the heart is denervated (cutting of both sympathetic and parasympathetic fibers to heart), from the basal rate of 70 per minute, the heart rate becomes 110 per minute, which is called the intrinsic heart rate. This indicates that normally vagal tone dominates over sympathetic tone for the control of heart rate.

4. What is Frank-Starling Law or Length-tension relationship of heart?
Ans: The force of contraction is directly proportional to the initial length of the muscle fiber, within the physiological limit.

5. What are the properties of cardiac muscle?
Ans: Automaticity, Rhythmicity, Conductivity, Contractility, Excitability, Distensibility, Long refractory period, Functional syncytium, Extrasystole and compensatory pause, All or none Law, Staircase phenomenon, Length-tension relationship, Frequency-force relationship, Load-velocity relationship

6. What are the mechanisms to explain Frank-Starling Law?
Ans: Four mechanisms:
   1. Increased actin-myosin interaction: With increased stretch of muscle fibers, the interaction between thick and thin filament increases, which increases the force of contraction.
   2. Opening of stretch-sensitive calcium channels: Opening of these channels on the muscle cell membrane increases the calcium influx and thus, force of contraction increases.
   3. Calcium-induced calcium release: Increase in intracellular calcium opens the calcium channels in the sarcoplasmic reticulum, causing rise in cytoplasmic calcium
   4. Increased affinity of troponin C for calcium: Stretch of myocardium increases the binding of troponin C to calcium that enhances the force of contraction.

7. What is the rate of discharge of potential pacemakers of heart per minute?
Ans: SA node (60 – 100), AV node (40 – 60), His bundle (25 – 40), Purkinje fiber (25 – 40), Ventricular muscle (15 – 3)

8. Why the cardiac muscle cannot be tetanized?
Ans: Duration of action potential of cardiac muscle is 250 ms, which is almost same as the duration of the mechanical response. The absolute refractory period of ventricular muscle is about 200 ms. Due to this long refractory period, a fresh contraction cannot occur before the completion of the previous mechanical response. Thus, mechanical responses of ventricular muscle cannot be summated, and therefore cardiac muscle cannot be tetanized.

9. Why the cardiac muscle is a functional syncytium?
Ans: Due to the presence of numerous gap junctions in cardiac muscle, all muscle fibers contract almost simultaneously, a functional syncytium. There are two syncytia in heart: atrial and ventricular syncytia.

10. What is post-extrasystolic potentiation?
Ans: The magnitude of contraction following the compensatory pause is usually a higher one as the ventricle gets more time for filling during the pause. The increased end-diastolic volume increases the force of contraction by Frank-Starling mechanism. This is called post-extrasystolic potentiation.

11. What is extrasystole and compensatory pause?
Ans: Extrasystole: When a stronger stimulus is applied in the relative refractory period, an extra contractile response occurs. This is called extrasystole.
Compensatory pause: The natural stimulus (impulse arising from the SA node) falls in the refractory period of the extrasystole and does not evoke a response. Therefore, the natural contraction is missed. This is why a long pause is recorded following the extrasystole, which is called compensatory pause.

12. What is All or none Law?
Ans: The cardiac tissue responds optimally or it does not respond at all irrespective of the strength of stimuli.

13. What is staircase phenomenon?
Ans: If the heart muscle is stimulated repeatedly keeping the interval between the stimuli just less than 10 s, the magnitude of first 3–4 contractions progressively increases, called staircase phenomenon. This is because the leftover calcium from the first contraction is added to the calcium released during the second contraction and results in greater amplitude. Also, the heat produced during preceding contraction decreases sarcoplasmic viscosity and facilitates the enzymatic activity that increases the height of succeeding contractions.

14. What is Frequency-force relationship?
Ans: Increase in force of contraction due to increase in heart rate (frequency) is known as frequency-force relationship. This is known as Bowditch phenomenon.

15. What is Load-velocity relationship?

Ans: The velocity of contraction is inversely proportional with the load that acts against it.

16. What are the effects of sympathetic stimulation on cardiac tissue?

Ans: Increases the rate of contraction (positively chronotropic), Increases the force of contraction (positively ionotropic), Increases the excitability (positively bathmotropic), Increases the conductivity (positively dromotropic)

17. Where are the fast response and slow response type of action potential observed ?

Ans: Fast response action potential: Atrial muscle, Ventricular muscle, Purkinje fibers

Slow response type of action potential: SA node and AV node

18. What are the phases and ionic basis of ventricular muscle action potential ?

Ans:

i) Phase 0: Phase of rapid depolarization and overshoot, due to opening of voltage-gated sodium channels

ii) Phase 1: Phase of initial rapid repolarization, due to closure of sodium channels and opening of K^+ channel

iii) Phase 2: Plateau phase or state of sustained depolarization, due to closure of K^+ channel and opening of voltage-gated calcium channels

iv) Phase 3: Phase of final repolarization, due to closure of calcium channels and closure of K^+ channel

v) Phase 4: Phase of restoration of membrane potential, due to opening of inward rectifying K^+ channels

19. What are the phases and ionic basis of SA nodal action potential ?

Ans: i) Phase 0: due to the opening of calcium channels

ii) Phase 3: due to closure of calcium channels & opening of the potassium channels

iii) Phase 4: Phase of slow diastolic depolarization. The early part of this phase is due to the decreased potassium conductance, Later part is due to *opening of transient calcium channels* and calcium sparks.

20. What is pacemaker potential (prepotential) and its ionic basis?

Ans: It is the spontaneous diastolic depolarization of the membrane potential following completion of each action potential.

In the initial part, the decline in potassium conductance (potassium decay) and opening of f' channels contribute, also calcium sparks and opening of sodium ion contribute to some extent. The later part is due to the opening of transient calcium channels.

21. What are the conduction velocity in cardiac tissues?

Ans: SA node (0.05 m/s), Internodal pathways (1 m/s), AV node (0.05 m/s), His bundle (1 m/s), Purkinje fibers (4 m/s), Ventricular muscle (1 m/s)

22. What are the effects of vagal and sympathetic stimulation on pacemaker potential?

Ans:

Vagal stimulation: Decreases the heart rate, decreases slope of the pacemaker potential and brings brings the RMP to more negative value.

Sympathetic stimulation: Increases the heart rate, increases slope of the pacemaker potential and brings the RMP to more positive value.

23. What are the ECG leads?

Ans: Direct lead: When a lead is directly applied to the surface of the heart, is called as direct lead.

Indirect leads: When the leads are applied away from the heart. They are limb leads (bipolar and unipolar), chest leads, and esophageal leads.

Bipolar limb leads (lead I, II, and III):

Lead I: Between the right arm (negative electrode) and the left arm (positive electrode).

Lead II: Between the right arm (negative electrode) and the left leg (positive electrode).

Lead III: Between the left arm (negative electrode) and the left leg (positive electrode)

Unipolar limb leads (aVR, aVL, and aVF):

aVR : Between the right arm (positive electrode) and left arm + left leg (negative electrode).

aVL : Between the left arm (positive electrode) and right arm + left leg (negative electrode).

aVF : Between the left foot (positive electrode) and right arm + left arm (negative electrode).

Chest leads:

V_1: In the right fourth intercostal space at the right border of the sternum.

V_2: In the left fourth intercostal space at the left border of the sternum.

V_3: At the midpoint between V_2 and V_4.

V_4: In the left fifth intercostal space on the midclavicular line.

V_5: In the left fifth intercostal space on the anterior axillary line.

V_6: In the left fifth intercostal space on the mid-axillary line.

24. What are the ECG waves and segments?

Ans: P wave is the first positive deflection in the ECG, produced by atrial depolarization

QRS complex consists of deflections produced by ventricular depolarization

T wave is the *positive deflection*, produced by ventricular repolarization.

PR Segment lies between the end of the P wave and the beginning of the QRS complex.

ST Segment lies between the end of the QRS complex and the beginning of the T wave.

25. What is PR interval and its significance?

Ans: PR interval is the interval between the beginning of the P wave to the beginning of the QRS complex. The duration of PR interval is from 0.12 to 0.20 second (average 0.18 s).

Significance: This represents *atrial depolarization and conduction through AV node.*

26. What is normal cardiac axis?

Ans: The normal direction of the mean cardiac vector ranges between –30 to +110 degrees

27. What are the conditions for axis deviation?

Ans: Right axis deviation(Right ventricular hypertrophy, Dextrocardia, WPW syndrome, Left posterior hemiblock)

Left axis deviation: (Left ventricular hypertrophy, Left anterior hemiblock, WPW syndrome, Inferior myocardial infarction, Obstructive airway disease)

28. What is idioventricular rhythm?

Ans: In complete heart block, a portion of ventricular muscle becomes the pacemaker and starts generating impulse at a rate of 15–40 beats/min. This is called idioventricular rhythm.\

29. What is sinus arrhythmia and its physiological basis?

Ans: Sinus arrhythmia is a normal physiological phenomenon referred to the increases in heart rate during inspiration and decreases in heart rate during expiration.

This *respiratory sinus arrhythmia* is explained by four mechanisms:

1. Alteration in autonomic activity: During inspiration, vagal activity decreases and sympathetic discharge increases. Thus, heart rate increases. During expiration, vagal activity increases that decreases heart rate.
2. Activation of Bainbridge reflex: During inspiration, decrease in intrathoracic pressure *increases venous return* to the right atrium and stretches the right atrial wall. This *stimulates atrial tachycardia producing receptors* and increases heart rate. Right atrial stretching also stretches SA node, which causes tachycardia.
3. Irradiation from inspiratory center: Increased irradiation of impulse *from inspiratory center to the vasomotor center* during inspiration increases the heart rate.
4. Activation of atrial stretch reflex: Increased venous return during inspiration *stimulates type B atrial stretch receptors*. This increases heart rate.

30. What are the types of heart blocks?

Ans: First Degree Heart Block: PR interval is abnormally prolonged.

Second Degree Heart Block

Mobitz Type I: Progressive prolongation of PR interval till a QRS complex is dropped.

Mobitz Type II: A ventricular beat occurs in every two or three atrial beats. Accordingly, it is called 2:1 or 3:1 block and so on.

Third Degree Heart Block

This is known as complete heart block as conduction of impulses from atria to ventricles is completely interrupted. Atria and ventricles beat separately. Therefore, in ECG P waves that appear regularly bear no relationship with QRS complexes.

31. What is ECG feature of acute myocardial infarction (AMI)?

Ans: The hallmark of ECG change in AMI is ST segment elevation.

32. What is Stokes-Adam syndrome?

Ans: In complete heart block, when the heart rate is as low as 15/min, blood circulation decreases that results in cerebral ischemia and causes fainting. This is called Stokes-Adam syndrome. After fainting, blood circulation to brain improves (due to assumption of lying posture of fainting) and patients regains consciousness. But again, he faints after sometimes.

33. What are the phases of cardiac cycle?

Ans: Cardiac cycle consists of the atrial systole and diastole, and the ventricular systole and diastole. The atrial diastole is merged in ventricular systole. Therefore, events of cardiac cycle are described in three phases:

i) Atrial systole

ii) Ventricular systole (the phase of isovolumetric contraction, the phase of rapid ejection, and the phase of reduced ejection)

iii) Ventricular diastole (the phase of isovolumetric relaxation, phase of rapid filling, phase of reduced filling)

34. What are the waves of Jugular venous pulse (JVP)?

Ans: JVP has five waves: three positive waves (a, c, and v) and two negative waves(x and y descents).

a wave: Due to atrial contraction.

c wave: Results from the bulging of tricuspid valve ring into the right atrium

v wave: The passive rise in pressure in the right atrium as venous return continues while the tricuspid valve remains closed.

x descent: caused by a fall of right atrial pressure due to relaxation of the right atrium.

y descent: due to fall in right atrial pressure when blood enters into the right ventricle as tricuspid valve opens.

35. Name some conditions of raised JVP.

Ans: Right-side heart failure, Obstruction of superior vena cava, Increase in circulating blood volume (Pregnancy, Over-enthusiastic treatment with IV fluids), Congestive heart failure, Constrictive pericarditis, Tricuspid incompetence

36. What is Cannon wave?

Ans: When amplitude of 'a' wave is abnormally big, it is called giant 'a' wave or cannon wave. It occurs when right atrium contracts against a closed tricuspid valve. It is seen in Complete heart block when atrial and ventricular systoles coincide and in Nodal rhythm when the atrium and ventricle are activated simultaneously.

37. What are the heart sounds?

Ans: First heart sound (S1) occurs due to vibration set up by: Sudden closure of the AV valves, rapid increase in tension in the ventricular muscles during isometric contraction acting on filled ventricles and turbulence created in the blood due to ventricular contraction.

Duration is about 0.15 second and frequency is 25 to 45 Hz. It is a soft sound heard as 'lub'

Second heart sound (S2) occurs due to closure of semilunar valves and rush of blood into the ventricles due to opening of the AV valves contributes.

Duration is about 0.12 second and frequency is 50 Hz. This is heard as 'dup'

Third heart sound (S3) is caused by the vibration setup in the ventricle during the early period of rapid ventricular filling.

Fourth heart sound (S4) is caused by atrial contraction.

38. Define stroke volume, cardiac output, end-diastolic volume, ejection fraction, end-systolic volume, cardiac index and cardiac reserve.

Ans: Stroke volume (SV) is defined as the volume of blood ejected by each ventricle with each beat.

Normal stroke volume is *about 70 ml.*

Cardiac output is defined as the amount of blood ejected by each ventricle per minute.

Cardiac output = stroke volume × heart rate.

So, if heart rate is 70 per minute, the cardiac output is 70 ml × 70 = 4900 ml (5 lit/min approximately).

Normal cardiac output in adults is 5–6 lit/min

End-diastolic volume (EDV) is the volume of blood remaining in each ventricle at the end of diastole.

Normal value: 130 ml

Ejection fraction is the percentage of end-diastolic volume ejected with each beat.

EF = SV/EDV × 100. Normal value: 65%.

End-systolic volume (ESV) is the volume of blood remaining in each ventricle at the end of systole.

Normal value: 50 ml.

Cardiac index is the cardiac output per square meter of body surface area.

Normal value: 3.2 L /min/m^2 of body surface area

Cardiac reserve It is the amount of blood that can be pumped by each ventricle in excess of normal cardiac output. Normal value: 15–25 lit/min in non-athletes and 20 to 40 lit/min in trained athletes.

39. What are the conditions where cardiac output is altered?

Ans: Conditions that increase cardiac output: Exercise, Anxiety, Emotion and excitement, Increased environmental temperature, After eating, Pregnancy

Conditions that decrease cardiac output: Standing from lying posture, Excessive sweating

Conditions that do not change cardiac output: Sleep, Mild to moderate change in environmental temperature

40. What are the factors that alter cardiac output?

Ans: Age: Cardiac output is less in elderly and in children.

Gender: CO is about 10% less in females.

Exercise: CO increases in exercise, due to sympathetic stimulation causing increased heart rate and stroke volume.

Excitement: CO increases in emotional excitements due to sympathetic stimulation.

Pregnancy: CO increases in pregnancy due to increase in blood volume that mainly occurs due to expansion of ECF volume.

After Eating: CO increases after eating due to increased metabolism.

Posture: Assuming standing posture from lying position decreases cardiac output due to accumulation of about 200–500 ml of blood blood in veins of lower extremities caused by effect of gravity.

41. What are the methods of measurement of cardiac output?

Ans: Direct method: By placing an electromagnetic flow meter in the ascending aorta or by using a cardiometer.

Indirect methods: Fick method, Indicator dilution method, Thermo-dilution method, Ballistocardiography, Echocardiography, X-ray method, Pulse-pressure method

42. What is Fick principle?

Ans: The amount of a substance taken up by an organ or by the whole body per unit of time is equal to the arteriovenous difference of the substance times blood flow.

The cardiac output is measured by applying Fick principle as:

CO = O_2 consumption (mL/min) ÷ arteriovenous difference of oxygen across the lungs

= 250 mL/min ÷ 50 mL/L = 5L/min

43. What are the factors affecting stroke volume?

Ans: It depends on three factors: Preload, Myocardial contractility and Afterload

Factors affecting Preload: i) Venous return (Skeletal muscle pump, Thoracic pump, Abdominal pump, ECF volume, Sympathetic activity, Right atrial pressure, Degree of filling of systemic circulation, Resistance to blood flow in venous system

ii) Atrial pump activity - increases by sympathetic stimulation

iii) Ventricular compliance (decreases in cardiomyopathies or infiltrative diseases of the heart, in constrictive pericarditis or pericardial effusion)

Factors affecting Myocardial contractility: Increase in myocardial contractility by increased ventricular muscle mass, Sympathetic stimulation, Digitalis, Catecholamines, Glucagon, Insulin, Thyroxine, caffeine and theophylline

Decrease in myocardial contractility by Acetylcholine, Hypercapnia, Hypoxia, Acidosis, General anesthetics, Toxins, Quinidine, procainamide and barbiturates

Factors affecting Afterload:

i) Vessel Diameter - The decrease in vessel diameter (vasoconstriction) increases peripheral resistance that decreases stroke volume. Stroke volume increases in vasodilation due to decreased afterload.

II) Viscosity of Blood - Increased viscosity as occurs in polycythemia, increases peripheral resistance and therefore decreases cardiac output. Cardiac output increases in anemia due to decreased viscosity.

44. What is normal HR?

Ans: 60-100 beats/min

45. What is bradycardia and what are the conditions for it?

Ans: Heart rate < 60/min is called bradycardia.

Physiological (Athletes, Fear, Grief, Very old age, Yogis)
Pathological (Myxedema. Increased intracranial pressure e.g. brain tumors, Obstructive jaundice, Different types of heart block, Drugs, e.g. digitalis)

46. What is tachycardia and what are the conditions for it?
Ans: Heart rate > 100/min is called tachycardia.
Physiological (Exercise, After eating, Anger, Emotion and excitement, Infants and children, Pregnancy, High environmental temperature)
Pathological (Fever, Anemia, Thyrotoxicosis, Beriberi, Paget's disease, Arterio-venous fistula, Heart failure, Paroxysmal atrial tachycardia, Ventricular or supra ventricular tachycardia)

47. What are the factors affecting heart rate?
Ans: i) Age: Heart rate is more in infants and children. After the age of sixty, heart rate decreases.
ii) Gender: Heart rate is comparatively less in females due to their relatively high parasympathetic tone and less basal metabolism.
iii) Diurnal Variation: Heart rate is more in the day, especially in the afternoon, and less in the night, especially during sleep. This difference is due to the less physical activity and sympathetic discharge in the night, and due to the low level of stress in sleep than in awakened state.
iv) Respiration: Heart rate is more during inspiration and less during expiration.
v) Body Temperature: Increase in body temperature increases heart rate and decrease in temperature decreases heart rate.
vi) Environmental Temperature: Heart rate is more in summer and less in winter.
vii) Food intake: Food intake increases heart rate by increasing body metabolism.
viii) Posture: Change in posture from supine to standing increases heart rate due to decreased stimulation of baroreceptors.
ix) Exercise: Heart rate increases in exercise due to sympathetic stimulation.

48. What is Water-Hammer Pulse?
Ans: Also called as Collapsing pulse or Corrigan's pulse. The pulse shows a rapid upstroke (ascent) and a rapid down stroke (descent).
Causes: Aortic incompetence, Hyperkinetic circulatory states e.g. thyrotoxicosis, Patent ductus arteriosus, Arteriovenous fistula, Ventricular septal defect

49. What is Pulsus Alternans?
Ans:
The pulse is regular, but the alternating beats are strong and weak
Causes: Left ventricular failure, Toxic carditis

50. What is edema?
Ans:
The accumulation of free fluid in excess in the interstitial tissues space is called edema.
Edema can occur due to increased filtration of fluid into interstitial tissues space and decreased removal of fluid from interstitial tissues space.

51. Define blood pressure.
Ans: Blood pressure is defined as the lateral pressure exerted by the column of blood on the wall of arteries.

52. Define systolic blood pressure and give its normal value.
Ans: Systolic BP is defined as the maximum pressure recorded during the cardiac cycle. As maximum pressure is recorded during systole, the pressure is called systolic pressure.
Normal systolic BP is 100 to 119 mm Hg in adults.

53. Define diastolic blood pressure and give its normal value.
Ans: Diastolic blood pressure is defined as the minimum pressure recorded during the cardiac cycle. As the minimum pressure is recorded during diastole, the pressure is called diastolic pressure.
Normal diastolic BP is 60 to 79 mm Hg in adults.

54. Define pulse pressure and give its normal value.
Ans: Pulse pressure (PP) is the difference between systolic and diastolic blood pressure.
Normal Value: 20 to 50 mmHg

55. Define mean arterial pressure and give its normal value.
Ans: Mean arterial pressure (MAP) is the average pressure recorded during the cardiac cycle.
It is calculated as: MAP = Diastolic Pressure + 1/3 PP. Normal Value: 75 to 105 mm Hg.

56. What are the factors affecting blood pressure?
Ans: Blood pressure = cardiac output × peripheral resistance
Alteration in cardiac output mainly affects systolic pressure and alteration in peripheral resistance mainly affects diastolic pressure.
Cardiac output = stroke volume × heart rate
The stroke volume is affected by preload, afterload and myocardial contractility, and the heart rate is affected by autonomic influences. (For details, see question no.43)
Peripheral resistance depends on diameter of blood vessel and viscosity of blood

57. What are the physiological variations of blood pressure?
Ans:
i) Age: Blood pressure increases with age.
ii) Gender: Blood pressure is comparatively less in females during their reproductive life due to the effect of progesterone that relaxes the smooth muscles of the blood vessels and estrogen that prevents atherosclerosis.
i) Eating: Blood pressure increases after a meal due to increased body metabolism that increases circulation and cardiac output following food intake.
ii) Sleep: Blood pressure is less during sleep than in the awakened state. When human being is awake, he is under the influence of stress and strain of life that increases BP.
iii) Emotion and Excitement: In emotion and excitement, increased sympathetic discharge increases blood pressure.

iv) Exercise: During exercise, the systolic pressure always rises due to increased cardiac output. Diastolic pressure increases in mild exercise due to vasoconstriction, but decreases in moderate to severe exercise due to metabolic vasodilation and increased body temperature.

v) Posture: On immediate standing from supine posture, blood pressure decreases due to venous pooling of blood in the lower limbs.

vi) Temperature: Blood pressure decreases in hot environment due to *cutaneous vasodilation* and increases in cold environment due to *vasoconstriction*.

vii) Pregnancy: Systolic pressure increases due to increased cardiac output as blood volume is increased in pregnancy. Diastolic pressure falls due to decreased peripheral resistance, as progesterone causes vasodilation.

58. What are the reflex regulation of blood pressure?

Ans: Baroreceptor reflex, Chemoreceptor reflex, Cushing reflex, Somatosympathetic reflex, Bainbridge reflex Atrial stretch reflex, Ventricular and pulmonary stretch reflexes, Nonphysiological chemoreflexes

59. What are the types of shock?

Ans: Hypovolemic Shock, Distributive Shock, Cardiogenic Shock, Obstructive Shock

60. What are the features of acute hemorrhagic shock?

Ans: Hypotension, Tachycardia, Rapid and thready pulse, Cold and pale skin, Tachypnea, Intense thirst, Restlessness.

SECTION VI - RESPIRATORY SYSTEM

MULTIPLE CHOICE QUESTIONS

1. The respiratory system has an upper respiratory tract, concerned with conduction of gases from the air to the lungs. The design of conduction structures is important for their function .The cartilages supporting the trachea are C-shaped rings. What is the reason for tracheal cartilages being C shaped?
   A. To allow the trachea to stretch when needed
   B. To enable a large volume of air to pass efficiently into the lungs
   C. To enable breathing when hanging upside down
   D. To prevent food entering the trachea when swallowing
   E. To prevent kinking during head movements

2. The alveoli, the minute balloon-like structures at the end of the terminal bronchioles and alveolar ducts, are the principal sites for gaseous exchange. The gap between the alveolar space and the pulmonary circulation is known as the gas–blood barrier (or the alveolar–capillary barrier). Which of the following statements is true about the gas–blood barrier?
   A. Consists of type I and type II alveolar cells A thick membrane between the alveolus and pulmonary circulation
   C. The gas-blood barrier is a fused membrane of alveolar epithelial cells and capillary epithelium
   D. CO2 diffuses from the alveoli into the blood across the barrier
   E. Has a surface area of about 10 m2

3. When analyzing a bronchoalveolar lavage sample, mononuclear phagocytic cells with dust inside mean that the sample is suitable. Where do these cells reside within the respiratory tract?
   A. Nasal breathing area and nasal olfactory area
   B. Nasopharynx and intrapulmonary bronchi
   C. Trachea and primary bronchi
   D. Terminal bronchi and respiratory bronchioles
   E. Alveolar duct and alveoli

4. What is the pressure in the alveolus when the transpulmonary pressure is 3.5 cmH2O and the pleural pressure is -8.5 cmH2O?
   A. -5 cmH2O 0 C. 5 cmH2O
   D. -12 cmH2O E. 10 cmH2O

5. A patient's pulmonary distensibility is measured with an esophageal balloon (a method to measure pleural pressure). When the patient has breathed in 500 mL, the esophageal pressure decreases from -3 cmH2O to -7 cmH2O residual functional capacity (RFC).What is the pulmonary distensibility?
   A. 1.67 L/cmH2O B. 0.71 L/cmH2O
   C. 0.5 L/cmH2O **D. 0.125 L/cmH2O**
   E. 1.45 L/cmH2O

6. If the oxygen consumption is 200 mL/min and the carbon dioxide production is 140 mL/min, what is the respiratory quotient?
   A. 60 mL/min B. 0.8 **C. 0.7**
   D. 143 mL/min E. 14

7. Breathing costs energy. About half of the work done during a respiratory cycle is dissipated during inspiration (as heat) to overcome airway resistance to airflow. The remaining energy is stored as potential energy in the elastic structures of the lungs and chest wall. Which of the following does not increase airflow resistance?
   A. Bronchospasm (constriction)
   B. Mediastinal tumours
   C. Laryngeal spasm
   D. Increased mucus secretion
   E. Laminar flow

8. If pleural pressure changes from -3 cmH2O to -7 cmH2O when residual functional capacity changes from one RFC value to another RFC +1 L when breathing, what is the pulmonary distensibility?
   A. 0.1 L/cmH2O B. 4 cmH2O/L
   C. 0.25 L/cmH2O D. 10 cmH2O/L
   E. 1.5 cmH2O/L

9. A person with early-stage lung disease has a circulating volume of 500 mL. What is the alveolar volume (VA) if the dead space (VD) doubles and the tidal volume (TV) remains the same? (Assume that the normal value of VD/TV is 0.25.)
   A. 150 mL **B. 250 ml** C. 300 mL
   D. 400 mL E. 500 mL

10. When alveolar ventilation (VA) decreases from 5 L/min to 2.5 L/min, PaCO2 will go from 40 mmHg to:
    A. 20 mmHg B. 60 mmHg
    C. 80 mmHg D. 100 mmHg
    E. 250 mmHg

11. With a respiratory rate of 15 breaths per minute, a standard volume of 500 mL and an anatomical dead space of 150 mL, what is the minute ventilation?
    A. 2.25 L/min B. 5.25 L/min
    C. 7.50 L/min D. 9.75 L/min
    E. 10.25

12. Ventilation is the movement of gas (air) in and out of the lungs; the rate of alveolar oxygen exchange depends on perfusion – the blood-flow through alveolar tissue. Which of the following statements about lung ventilation and perfusion is true?
    A. Perfusion at the apices of the lungs is higher than at the bases of upright normal lungs
    B. Ventilation at the apices of the lungs is higher than at the bases of upright normal lungs
    C. The ventilation/perfusion ratio at the apices is higher than at the bases of upright normal lungs

D. Blood in the pulmonary capillaries continues to be re-oxygenated despite widespread ventilation–perfusion mismatch
E. A reduced level of carbon dioxide in the blood may result from widespread ventilation–perfusion mismatch

13. A 44-year-old poly-traumatized patient receives multiple blood transfusions for severe bleeding. How would this treatment affects the patient's O2 dissociation curve?
A. It shifts to the left B. It shifts to the right
C. No change D. It shifts downwards
E. It shifts upwards

14. Which of the following factors DOES NOT affect alveolar partial pressure of oxygen directly?
A. PaCO2 B. Atmospheric pressure
C. Circulating volume D. Inlet oxygen fraction
E. Oxygen consumption and production of carbon dioxide (R)

15. The alteration in the structure in one sub-unit by binding with O2 alters the structure of the other sub-units, increasing their affinity for haemoglobin. Factors favouring O2 unloading from haemoglobin include: hydrogen ions temperature 2,3 diphosphoglycerate (2,3-DPG).Which of the following statements is true, if the concentration of 2,3-DPG increases?
A. Increased Hb affinity for O2
B. O2 released less easily from red cells
C. Increased levels in transfused blood
D. The affinity of oxygen to haemoglobin decreases
E. No change

16. In normal humans, the partial pressures of arterial oxygen (O2) and carbon dioxide (CO2) are kept within normal limits. Variation in either direction triggers the respiratory centres; the breathing pattern is modified to vary O2 input or CO2 output. What modifies respiratory response when climbing a mountain?
A. Acidosis B. Anoxia
C. Hypercapnia **D. Hypocapnia**
E. Hypoxia

17. Respiratory control for effective gas exchange to maintain a normal paO2 and a normal paCO2 is regulated by the nervous system. Central and peripheral chemoreceptors relay changes in partial pressures to the brainstem. Which of the following is the rationale for not giving pure oxygen to a patient with chronic emphysema?
A. Pure oxygen is combustible and likely to explode
B. Pure oxygen on emphysematous lungs can cause alveoli rupture
C. Pure oxygen if given via face mask can cause 'the bends' at sea level
D. Pure oxygen will dry the mucus membranes and increase the likelihood of respiratory infections
E. Pure oxygen in emphysema can lead to coma

18. A person is flying at 3000 m (500 mmHg barometric pressure) in a non-pressurized airplane, breathing air. If alveolar ventilation is normal, what would the arterial oxygen saturation be?
A. 97 mmHg
B. 90 mmHg
C. 50 mmHg
D. 45 mmHg
E. 40 mmHg

19. A person that is not conditioned breathes ambient air at an altitude of 4,500 m (barometric pressure = 483). When walking, alveolar ventilation and metabolism increases twice as much. What is the pO2 in the alveoli?
A. 42 mmHg
B. 66 mmHg
C. 91 mmHg
D. 152 mmHg
E. 183 mmHg

20. Cyanosis occurs in the presence of high levels of deoxygenated haemoglobin and is clinically detectable in a patient by observation of a bluish discolouration. Which of the following is the correct amount of deoxygenated haemoglobin at which cyanosis can be clinically detectable?
A. 0.05 g/dL B. 0.5 g/dL **C. 5.0 g/dL**
D. 25 g/dL E. 50 g/dL

21. A 16-year-old patient has difficulty breathing, watery nasal discharge, wheezing, and chest tightness, without fever. Spirometry is performed, showing reduced FEV1 with FEV1/FVC quotient alteration. FEV1 improves by 15% after administration of a bronchodilator. A chest radiograph was also performed. The family mentions that they bought a cat several weeks ago. You suspect allergic asthma.What serum antibody would you expect to see increased to confirm the diagnosis?
A. IgA B. IgG C. IgM
D. IgE E. IgD

22. A 56-year-old woman has worked in a photography store developing films for the past 20 years. She has a long history of shortness of breath and chronic cough which have progressively worsened. The FEV1 and FVC values were reduced, although the FEV1/FVC quotient was within the normal range. The diffusing capacity measured with DLCO was low, 15 mL/min/mmHg. Bronchoalveolar lavage and tissue biopsy were performed. The lavage sample showed a high number of abnormally looking macrophages as well as dead macrophages.What type of anatomopathological alteration would you expect to find?
A. Peribronchial inflammation with eosinophils
B. Granulomatous-type lesion in terminal bronchioles with interstitial fibrosis and large foamy macrophages
C. Accumulation of interstitial edema fluid with neutrophil infiltration
D. Emphysematous lesion with large alveoli and minimal interstitial fibrosis
E. All of the above answers are false

23. A 65-year-old woman, with a history of 2 packs/day smoking for 30 years, is diagnosed with chronic obstructive pulmonary disease. It is very likely that she may have increased mucus viscosity due to:
    A. Bronchoconstriction
    B. Stimulation of the parasympathetic fibers of the bronchial glands
    C. Stimulation of sympathetic nerves
    D. Abnormal breathing pattern
    E. Smooth muscle stimulation

24. A 65-year-old woman, with a history of 2 packs/day smoking for 30 years, is diagnosed with chronic obstructive pulmonary disease. There is evidence that she uses the accessory respiratory muscles for breathing, which is produced by:
    A. Decreased work of breathing due to obstruction to the respiratory flow
    B. Increased work of breathing due to neuromuscular union dysfunction
    C. Increased work of breathing due to an obstruction of the respiratory flow that requires active contraction of the expiratory muscles
    D. Abnormal breathing pattern
    E. Increased work of breathing due to an obstruction of the respiratory flow that requires active contraction of the inspiratory muscles

25. Respiratory diseases are classified as obstructive or restrictive. Pulmonary fibrosis is an example of restrictive respiratory disease where the available lung volume for gaseous exchange is reduced, or restricted. Which of the following parameters of respiratory function tests are significantly lower than normal in pulmonary fibrosis?
    A. Peak expiratory flow rate
    B. Forced expiratory volume in litres (FEV1)
    C. Anatomical dead space
    D. Forced expiratory ratio (FEV1/FVC)
    E. Carbon dioxide transfer

26. A 56-year-old woman has worked in a photography store developing films for the past 20 years. She has a long history of shortness of breath and chronic cough, which have progressively worsened. The FEV1 and FVC values were reduced, although the FEV1/FVC quotient was within the normal range. The diffusing capacity measured with DLCO was low, 15 mL/min/mmHg. Bronchoalveolar lavage and tissue biopsy were performed. The lavage sample showed a high number of abnormally looking macrophages as well as dead macrophages.What type of lung disease do you suspect?
    A. Restrictive disease
    B. Obstructive disease
    C. Infectious disease
    D. Lung cancer
    E. Genetic hereditary diseas

* * *

VIVA / SHORT QUESTION

1. What are the muscles of inspiration and expiration?
   Ans: Muscles of inspiration: Diaphragm, External intercostal muscles, scalenes, Sternocleidomastoids
   Muscles of expiration: Abdomen, Internal intercostals

2. What is dead space?
   Ans: The space within the airways that do not allow gas exchange with pulmonary capillary blood to occur.

3. What is anatomical dead space?
   Ans: The fraction of tidal volume that occupies the conducting airways does not take part in gas exchange. For each 500 ml of air inhaled, about 150 ml remains in the conducting airways, which is not used in gas exchange.

4. What is physiological dead space?
   Ans: Some alveoli due to various reasons have little or no blood supply. Therefore, air in these alveoli also becomes part of the wasted air. The volume of air in these alveoli is referred to as alveolar dead space. The sum of the anatomical dead space and alveolar dead space is called physiological dead space.

5. What are the layers of alveolar-capillary membrane?
   Ans: The layers are Alveolar surfactant, Layer of alveolar epithelial cells, Basement membrane of alveolar epithelium, A thin layer of interstitial fluid, Basement membrane of capillary endothelium, Layer of capillary endothelial cells, Plasma, Red cell membrane, Intra-erythrocyte fluid, Hemoglobin molecule.

6. How is oxygen transported in blood??
   Ans: Oxygen is transported as physically dissolved in the plasma (2%) and in combination with hemoglobin (Hb) in the red cell (98%).

7. What are the factors that Shift Oxy-Hb dissociation Curve to right?
   Ans: Increased temperature, Decreased pH, Increased $PCO_{2,}$ Increased 2,3-DPG, Hypoxia

8. What are the factors that Shift Oxy-Hb Dissociation Curve to left?
   Ans: Decreased temperature, Increased pH, Decreased $PCO_{2,}$ Decreased 2,3-DPG, Fetal Hb, Carbon monoxide.

9. What is Bohr Effect?
   Ans: At the tissue level, CO_2 enters the blood and shifts the Oxy-Hb dissociation curve to right. This helps in unloading of oxygen from Hb and facilitates tissue oxygenation. This phenomenon is called Bohr Effect.

10. How is CO_2 transported in blood??
Ans: CO_2 is transported as physically dissolved in the plasma (7%), as bicarbonate ions in plasma and in red cells (70%) and as carbamino protein complexes (23%).

11. What is chloride shift or Hamburger shift?
Ans: Inside the red blood cells, as carbonic acid readily dissociates to HCO_3^- and H^+, bicarbonate concentration increases in red cells. HCO_3^- leaves the red blood cells and in exchange chloride (Cl^-) enters the cell from the plasma to maintain electrical neutrality. The chloride movement in exchange for HCO_3^- is known as the chloride shift.

12. What is Haldane effect?
Ans: When blood passes through pulmonary capillaries, oxygen diffuses into the blood and forms Oxy-Hb. Oxygenation of Hb shifts the CO_2 dissociation curve to right and Hb begins to lose CO_2. This is called Haldane effect.

13. What are the medullary respiratory centers?
Ans: Medulla has dorsal respiratory group (DRG) and ventral respiratory group (VRG) of neurons.
DRG contains inspiratory neurons. VRG has rostral expiratory, middle inspiratory and caudal expiratory regions. In addition, central pattern generator (CPG) is located in the medulla and it generates normal respiratory rhythm.

14. What are the respiratory centers in pons?
Ans: Two respiratory centers: pneumotaxic and apneustic.
Pneumotaxic center coordinates respiration by switching between inspiration and expiration, and it inhibits apneustic center. Apneustic center strongly activates medullary inspiratory center.

15. What is the effect of vagus nerve on respiration?
Ans: The afferent vagal impulse inhibits the medullary inspiratory neurons. Therefore, magnitude of inspiration increases following vagotomy and vagal stimulation results in inhibition of respiration.

16. What are the peripheral chemoreceptors?
Ans: Peripheral chemoreceptors are located in the carotid and aortic bodies. They respond to changes in PO_2, PCO_2 and pH in arterial blood. They are more sensitive to decreased arterial PO_2 (hypoxia).

17. What are the central chemoreceptors?
Ans: Central chemoreceptors are located in ventrolateral medulla. CO_2 that enters the CSF is immediately hydrated to form H_2CO_3, which dissociates to form H^+ and HCO_3^-. Central chemoreceptors respond to change in the H^+.

18. What are the changes at high-altitude?
Ans: Hyperventilation, urine becomes alkaline, increased red cell production, increased concentration of 2,3-DPG in the red cells, Increased cardiac output, vasodilation, Increase in number of capillaries.

19. What are the features of Chronic Mountain Sickness (Monge's Disease)?
Ans: Pulmonary hypertension, malaise, fatigue, hypervolemia, exercise intolerance, polycythemia, right ventricular hypertrophy, heart failure and cerebral edema.

20. What are the types of hypoxia?
Ans: Hypoxic hypoxia, Anemic hypoxia, Stagnant hypoxia, Histotoxic hypoxia.

21. What are the hazards of deep sea diving?
Ans: They are: Nitrogen narcosis, High pressure nervous syndrome, Acute oxygen toxicity, Dysbarism, Air embolism.

22. What are the features of Dysbarism /Caissons Disease/ Decompression sickness)?
Ans: Severe pain in muscles and joints due to nitrogen bubbles, sensory and motor deficits due to decreased blood flow to brain and spinal cord, respiratory compression, and myocardial ischemia.

23. What are the prevention and treatment of Decompression sickness?
Ans: Prevented by slow recompression (gradual ascent to the sea level).
Treatment: Recompressed immediately in a pressurized cabin, followed by slow decompression. Hyperbaric oxygen is also helpful.

24. What is periodic breathing?
Ans: Cyclical repetition of apnea and hyperpnea in normal individuals is called periodic breathing. This is typically seen following voluntary hyperventilation performed for 2 to 3 min.

25. What is Cheyne-Stokes respiration?
Ans: Periodic breathing that occurs in diseases and abnormal condition is called Cheyne-Stokes respiration. It occurs in heart failure, uremia, brain diseases, unacclimatized persons at high altitude, premature infants and during deep sleep in some people.

SECTION VII - GASTROINTESTINAL SYSTEM

MULTIPLE CHOICE QUESTIONS

1. A 28-year-old medical student eats a cheeseburger, chips and chocolate milkshake. The food stimulates the release of various gastrointestinal hormones. The presence of fat, carbohydrates, or proteins in the duodenum stimulates the release of a hormone from the duodenal mucosa. Which hormone is it?
   A. Cholecystokinin (CCK)
   B. Glucose-dependent insulinotropic peptide (GLIP)
   C. Gastrin
   D. Motiline
   E. Secretin

2. An 87-year-old farmer has had eggs, bacon, ham, semolina with cheese, chips, crackers with jam, butter and coffee for breakfast. Which of the following hormones is released by the presence of fats and proteins in the small intestine and helps decrease gastric emptying?
   A. Cholecystokinin (CCK)
   B. Glucose-dependent insulinotropic peptide (GLIP)
   C. Gastrin
   D. Motiline
   E. Secretin

3. Although not completely understood, the inhibitory hormones, known as enterogastrones, including intestinal hormones secretin, cholecystokinin and gastric inhibitory peptides, probably acting together during feeding, contribute to the inhibition of gastric function (secretions and motility). Which of the following stimulates cholecystokinin secretion?
   A. Presence of carbohydrates in the duodenum
   B. Hydrochloric acid in the duodenum
   C. Fatty acids and monoglyceride in the duodenum
   D. Vitamins D, E, K and A in the duodenum
   E. Water (hypotonic solution) in the duodenum

4. A 50-year-old alcoholic man has had recurrent episodes of pancreatitis that reduce the production of pancreatic enzymes after eating a mixed meal. He also reports diarrhea, and feces containing high concentrations of triglycerides but no intact starch. The duodenal aspirate obtained after a meal also shows that starch is digested properly. Assuming that during pancreatitis there is a decrease in the production of all pancreatic enzymes, what structures constitute an alternative source of enzyme activity capable of digesting starch?
   A. Brunner's glands
   B. Brush border of enterocytes
   C. Gallbladder
   D. Parietal cells
   E. Salivary glands

5. A patient with a history of gastroesophageal reflux disease has received chronic treatment with a proton pump inhibitor that greatly reduces gastric acid secretion. Compared to a normal person the patient will have an increased risk of one of the following:
   A. Enteric infections
   B. Fat malabsorption
   C. Carbohydrate malabsorption
   D. Lactose intolerance
   E. Cystic fibrosis

6. Which of the following changes in the ability of gastrin, acetylcholine, and histamine to stimulate acid secretion is caused by the administration of a histamine H2receptor antagonist? Gastrin Acetylcholine Histamine A ↑ ↓ ↓ B ↔ ↓ ↔ C ↓ ↑ ↓ D ↓ ↓ ↓ E ↔ ↓ ↓ 2receptor antagonist?
   A. Option A
   B. Option B
   C. Option C
   D. Option D
   E. Option E

7. A 55-year-old male comes in with abdominal pain and hematemesis. The results of the abdominal exploration were relatively benign, but abdominal x-rays showed visceral perforation. The endoscopy revealed a gastric ulcer with chronic perforation, through which it was possible to see the liver. Which of the following is a precursor to the formation of the gastric ulcer?
   A. Retrograde loss of hydrogen ions
   B. Secretion of mucus
   C. Proton pump inhibition
   D. Narrow joints between cells
   E. Vagotomy

8. A 27-year-old woman eats a healthy dinner. The answers indicate the rate of acid secretion before and at various times after the meal. At which of these times is the pH of the stomach contents lower? Moment Acid secretion rate A Before a meal 2 mEq H+/h B 30 min after the meal 35 mEq H+/h C 60 min after the meal 29 mEq H+/h D 90 min after the meal 20 mEq H+/h E 120 min after meal 10 mEq H+/h
   A. Option A
   B. Option B
   C. Option C
   D. Option D
   E. Option E

9. A 77-year-old woman with high abdominal pain and blood in the stool has been taking NSAIDs for her arthritis. An endoscopy shows a patchy gastritis all over the stomach. Biopsies were negative for H. pylori. For which of the following responses did intravenously

administered pentagastrin cause a lower than expected (i.e., lower than normal) increase?

A. Growth of the duodenal mucosa
B. Gastric secretion of acid
C. Gastrin secretion
D. Secretion of pancreatic enzymes
E. Growth of the pancreas

10. Pancreatic enzymes are secreted in the acinar cells, then washed into the lumen of the ducts by a small amount of isotonic solution. The pancreatic duct system produces large quantities of bicarbonate rich fluid. Secretin stimulates the duct cells to enhance HCO3 secretion. In which of the following cells is secretin synthesized?

A. I cells
B. D cells
C. Alpha cells
D. S cells
E. Beta cells

11. Enzyme secretion by the exocrine pancreas occurs in three phases: cephalic, gastric and intestinal. Each phase is regulated by stimulatory and inhibitory mechanisms. In the intestinal phase, which one of the following stimulates the release of the inhibitory enzyme peptide YY?

A. pH
B. Presence of fat in the terminal ileum and colon
C. Secretin
D. Bile salts
E. High ileal protein content

12. A 35-year-old woman enters the emergency department due to severe pain in the upper right quadrant. The woman measures 155 cm and weighs 115 kg (BMI = 46.5). She claims that her stool is clay-colored and her urine is orange. Physical examination shows an enlarged liver and jaundiced conjunctiva. CBC indicates elevation of serum bilirubin. In which of the following areas in this patient is the absorption of bile salts most likely to decrease to a maximum degree?

A. Option A
B. Option B
C. Option C
D. Option D
E. Option E

13. In an experiment, a researcher infuses a solution of conjugated bile acids into the portal vein of a rat, so that its concentration increases to about twice the normal level. He obtains hepatic bile samples from the rat before and after infusion. Before infusion the concentrations of bile acids (BA), phosphatidylcholine (PC) and cholesterol (col.) are 30, 9 and 3 units per ml, respectively. What would be the predicted concentrations of PC and col. in bile after infusion of BA?

A. PC: 9; col: 3
B. PC: 18; col: 3
C. PC: 9; col: 6
D. PC: 18; col: 6
E. PC: 3; col: 9

14. During the process of bilirubin conjugation, bilirubin binds to albumin and is captured by the liver through the bloodstream. What is the name of the liver enzyme that picks up bilirubin (not water-soluble) and produces bilirubin diglucuronide (water-soluble)?

A. UDP-glucuronyl transferase
B. Hemoxygenase
C. Biliverdin reductase
D. Vitamin K epoxide reductase
E. Glutathione reductase

15. Vomiting (emesis) is a complex series of responses in the gastrointestinal tract, respiratory tract and abdominal musculature leading to the forceful expulsion of gastric, and sometimes duodenal, contents. The vomiting centre receives significant neural input from which of the following sources?

A. The cerebellum
B. The acoustic system
C. The visual cortex
D. The peripheral organs such as the lungs and muscles
E. The chemoreceptor trigger zone (CTZ)

16. In a diagnostic test, a digestologist uses an endoscope to deliver a diluted acid bolus into the distal esophagus. The bolus is enough to produce esophageal dilation. In a normal person this bolus will be eliminated from the esophagus predominantly by one of the following mechanisms, which one?:

A. Primary peristalsis
B. Swallowing
C. Secondary peristalsis
D. Relaxation of the lower esophageal sphincter
E. Receptive relaxation

17. A college student notices that when he sits down for dinner he is often assaulted by an intense desire to defecate. The proximal signal that triggers the reflex arc that promotes this response most likely originates in one of these elements of the system involved in the integrated response to a meal, which one?:

A. Brain
B. Pharynx
C. Esophagus
D. Stomach
E. Duodenum

18. A scientist genetically modifies a mouse so that it lacks the hormone secretin. Compared to a normal animal, which of the following would you expect to be increased in the mutant mouse?

A. pH of the pancreatic pathways secretion
B. Volume of pancreatic secretion
C. pH of duodenal content
D. Susceptibility to duodenal erosions and ulcerations
E. Contractility of the gallbladder

19. A newborn does not expel meconium in the first 24 hours. The child's abdomen stretches and they begin to vomit. Other tests lead to the diagnosis of Hirschsprung's disease. Where in the intestine is an obstruction most likely to be found?
    A. Ascending colon
    B. Ileocecal sphincter
    C. Lower esophageal sphincter
    D. Pylorus
    E. Sigmoid colon

20. A 36-year-old woman suffers a severe spinal cord injury in a traffic accident. She needs the help of enemas to defecate. Which of the following processes does not occur in this woman?
    A. Contraction of the rectum
    B. Contraction of the sigmoid colon
    C. Contraction of the external anal sphincter
    D. Contraction of the descending colon
    E. Relaxation of the internal anal sphincter

21. A 52-year-old male eats a healthy meal. Approximately 20 minutes later, he notices the urge to defecate. Which of the following reflexes causes the urge to defecate when the stomach is stretched?
    A. Duodenocolic reflex
    B. Enterogastric reflex
    C. Gastrocolic reflex
    D. Ileocecal reflex
    E. Intestino-intestinal reflex

22. A newborn does not expel meconium in the first 24 hours. Their abdomen is distended and they start vomiting. Hirschsprung's disease is suspected. Which of the following factors is virtually absent in the contracted segment of the colon of this patient?
    A. Blood flow
    B. Circular smooth muscle
    C. Neurons of the myenteric plexus
    D. Mucous
    E. Serosa

23. A 43-year-old medical student suffers a spinal cord injury in an accident. They start defecation by inserting a Foley balloon probe into the rectum and inflating the balloon with a 50 mL syringe. What reflex is stimulated by the balloon in this patient?
    A. Duodenocolic reflex
    B. Enterogastric reflex
    C. Ileocecal reflex
    D. Intrinsic defecation reflex
    E. Spinal cord reflex

24. By what chemical process are carbohydrates, fats and digested proteins absorbed into sufficiently small components?
    A. Deamination
    B. Decarboxylation
    C. Hydrolysis
    D. Oxidation
    E. Phosphorylation

VIVA / SHORT QUESTION

1. Name some GI hormones.
   Ans: Gastrin, Cholecystokinin, Secretin, Glucagon, GIP and VIP.

2. List the Functions of saliva.
   Ans:
   1. Saliva contains ptyalin (salivary amylase), which causes splitting of starch.
   2. Saliva prevents oral infection as it contains lysozyme, IgA, and lactoferrin.
   3. Saliva keeps the mouth cavity and tongue moist, which facilitates speech.
   4. Saliva increases the taste of food.
   6. Saliva contains bicarbonate which buffers gastric acid to some extent in the stomach, and therefore reduces heart burn.
   7. Proline rich protein in saliva protects enamel of the teeth.
   8. Saliva prevents injury to buccal mucosa by diluting the hot and irritant food materials.
   9. In animals, salivation (panting) is an important process of dissipation of heat and therefore, has contribution in temperature regulation.
   10. Saliva excretes certain heavy metals, thiocyanate and morphine from the body.

3. List the Functions of stomach.
   Ans:
   1. Temporary storage of food
   2. Grinding and mixing of food
   3. Controlled emptying of food
   4. Secretion of hydrochloric acid
   5. HCl in the stomach converts ferric form of iron into ferrous form
   6. Kills the microorganism
   7. Activates pepsinogen to pepsin
   8. Secretes intrinsic factor
   9. Stomach helps in absorption of water and lipid soluble substances, such as alcohol and few drugs.

4. Give the composition of Gastric Juice.
   Ans: Water (99.5%), Solids (0.5%). Solids contain inorganic and organic substances.
   Inorganic Constituents: Anions are Cl^-, PO_4^{3-}, SO_4^{2-}, and HCO_3^-; and cations are H^+, Na^+, K^+, Ca^{2+}, and Mg^{2+}.
   Organic Constituents: Pepsinogen, intrinsic factor, mucin, rennin, gastric lipase, gelatinase, carbonic anhydrase, and lysozyme.

5. What is post-prandial alkaline tide?
   Ans: As for each H^+ secreted into the gastric lumen, one HCO^{3-} is reabsorbed into the plasma, with increase in the rate of HCl secretion, the level of HCO^{3-} increases in the blood. Consequently, following a meal that stimulates gastric acid secretion, pH of blood increases. As blood becomes alkaline, the urine becomes alkaline. This alkalinization of urine is called post-prandial alkaline tide.

6. What are the factors that increase HCl secretion?
   Ans:
   i) Luminal Factors (Distension of stomach, Products of protein digestion)
   ii) Hormonal Factors: Acetylcholine, Gastrin and Histamine
   iii) Neural Factors (Vagal stimulation - cholinergic & noncholinergic)
   iv) Blood borne (Epinephrine)

7. What are the factors that inhibit HCl secretion?
   Ans: i) Luminal Factors - Increased acid content (highly acidic chyme)
   ii) Hormonal Factors (locally acting) - Somatostatin
   iii) Blood-borne Factors - Secretin, GIP, Glucagon

8. What are the phases of gastric acid secretion?
   Ans: Three phases: Cephalic, Gastric and Intestinal

9. How is the cephalic phase of gastric secretion regulated?
   Ans: The cephalic phase of gastric secretion is elicited by smell, sight, thought, taste and chewing of food. This phase accounts for 30–50% of total gastric secretion.

10. How is the gastric phase of gastric secretion regulated?
    Ans: Stimulated by products of digestion, distension of the stomach, and decreased by the acidic pH of the chyme. Gastric phase accounts for 50–60 % of gastric secretion.

11. How is the gastric phase of intestinal secretion regulated?
    Ans: Initial part of intestinal phase is stimulatory to gastric secretion, but later part is inhibitory. Intestinal phase accounts for about 10% of gastric secretion.

12. Name some gastric function tests.
    Ans: Examination of gastric contents, Test for gastric acid secretion, Tests for pepsin, mucous, intrinsic factor, Tests for gastrin, Visualization of the interior of stomach, Tests for gastric motility and electrical activities (gastrography), Obtaining biopsy from the suspected tissue.

13. Name some tests for gastric acid secretion.
    Ans: Histamine stimulation test, Pentagastrin test, Insulin test (Hollander test)

14. What are the treatments of peptic ulcer?
    Ans:
    i) H2 receptor antagonists: Ranitidine, cimetidine, famotidine, and nizatidine
    ii) Proton-pump blocker (H^+-K^+ATPase inhibitor): omeprazole.
    iii) Sucralfate: It provides a protective layer on the ulcer and promotes ulcer healing.
    iv) Antibiotics to kill H. pylori has provided promising result.

15. What are the functions of pancreatic enzymes?

Ans:

i) For lipid digestion (Lipase, Phospholipase, Cholesterol hydrolase)

ii) For protein digestion (Trypsin, Chymotrypsin, Elastase, Carboxypeptidase, Ribonuclease, Deoxyribonuclease)

iii) For carbohydrate digestion (Amylase)

16. What are the factors regulating pancreatic secretion?

Ans:

i) Hormonal factors: Cholecystokinin stimulates enzymatic pancreatic secretion, whereas secretin stimulates pancreatic secretion rich in water and bicarbonate.

ii) Neural factors: Parasympathetic stimulation increases secretion whereas sympathetic stimulation decreases pancreatic secretion.

17. What are the functions of Liver?

Ans:

1. Secretory functions: Liver forms and secretes bile into biliary tract.
2. Metabolic functions: Liver is involved in metabolism of major nutrients such as carbohydrate, fat, proteins, and fat soluble and water-soluble vitamins.
3. Synthetic functions: Liver is the major organ for the synthesis of proteins that include clotting factors, acute phase proteins, hormone binding proteins, lipids, carbohydrates, vitamins and bile salts.
4. Storage functions: Liver stores glucose, protein, fat, and vitamins.
5. Detoxifying action: Liver detoxifies many chemicals and toxins released from infecting organisms.
6. Degradation of drugs and chemicals: Liver degrades drugs, enzymes, hormones, cytokines and various other chemicals.
7. Excretory function: Liver excretes bile pigments, cholesterol, and some metals.
8. Immunity: Kupffer cells of liver are part of mononuclear phagocyte system
9. Endocrine functions: Liver converts vitamin D_3 to 25-hydroxyvitamin D_3 and T_4 to T_3.

18. What is the composition of bile?

Ans: Bile salts, Bile pigments, Cholesterol, Inorganic salts, Fatty acids and fat, Alkaline phosphatase, Cations (Na^+, K+, Ca^{2+} and Mg^{2+}), Anions (HCO^{3-}, C^{l-}, SO_4^{2-} and PO_4^{3-})

19. What are the differences between hepatic and gall bladder bile?

Ans:	**Hepatic bile**	**Gall bladder bile**
1. pH	Alkaline (8–8.5)	Acidic (about 7)
2. Water content	98%	85%
3. Solids	2 g%	10–15g%
4. Bile salts & pigments	Less	More

20. What are the bile acids?

Ans:

i) Primary bile acids are cholic acid and chenodeoxycholic acid.

ii) Secondary bile acids are deoxycholic acid and lithocholic acid.

21. What are the bile salts?

Ans: Na^+taurocholate, Na^+glycocholate, K^+taurocholate and K^+-glycocholate

22. 22.What are the functions of bile?

Ans: Bile helps in absorption of lipids from intestine by forming micelles, Bile salts in bile are important choleretics (increase bile secretion), Bile promotes absorption of fat-soluble vitamins (A, D, E, and K), Bile salts activate pancreatic lipase, Bile pigments (bilirubin and biliverdin) are responsible for greenish-yellow coloration of gall bladder that helps to identify the organ especially in small animals.

23. 23.What is enterohepatic circulation of bile acids and salts?

Ans: Bile acids and salts are absorbed from the intestine and re-excreted in the bile, and this cycle is repeated so many times, which is called enterohepatic circulation of bile acids and salts.

24. What are the choleretics?

Ans: Bile salts, Secretin, Vagal stimulation, Secretin (increases aqueous component of bile)

25. What are the cholagogues?

Ans: Cholecystokinin, Fatty acids.

26. What are the motilities of intestine?

Ans: Segmentation, Peristalsis, Migrating myoelectric complex, Contraction of the muscularis mucosa, Villus contractions, and Movements due to intestinal reflexes.

27. What is the function of segmentation ?

Ans: Segmentation contractions effectively mix chyme with pancreatic and intestinal secretions.

28. What is the function of peristalsis?

Ans: The function of peristaltic movements is to propel chyme in forward direction.

29. What is migrating myoelectric (motor) complex?

Ans: The bursts of intense electrical and contractile activity, once in about every 90 minutes is called migrating myoelectric complex.

30. What is Hirschsprung disease or congenital megacolon or aganglionosis?

Ans: The entire neuronal plexuses in the wall of the colon are congenitally absent. It manifests as abdominal distention, anorexia and lassitude. In severe cases, symptoms appear in newborns as early as third day after birth. It is treated by surgical dilation.

SECTION VIII- ENDOCRINE PHYSIOLOGY

MULTIPLE CHOICE QUESTIONS

1. An elderly person, due to confusion, takes an overdose of a drug designed to block both the uptake of cholesterol in the digestive tract and the synthesis of cholesterol by all cells. After 24 h the patient has severe hypocholesterolemia (i.e. has very low concentrations of circulating cholesterol).This effect is transient; when the effect of the drug disappears there will be a rebound of hormone concentrations. Which of the following mechanisms is primarily responsible for the stability of hormone concentrations in this situation?
   A. Liver replacement
   B. Negative feedback reaction
   C. Peripheral conversion
   D. Kidney excretion
   E. Melatonin

2. Endocrine diseases are often due to the loss of a hormone (i.e., a hormone deficiency). Which of the following would produce an endocrine disease similar to a protein hormone deficiency without any deficiency in the concentration of the circulating protein hormone?
   A. Inactive prohormone convertase
   B. Defective exocytosis machinery
   C. Loss of blood-carrying proteins
   D. Defective receiver
   E. Mutation with no function of the corresponding hormone gene

3. An elderly person, due to confusion, takes an overdose of a drug designed to block both the uptake of cholesterol in the digestive tract and the synthesis of cholesterol by all cells. After 24 h the patient has severe hypocholesterolemia (i.e. has very low concentrations of circulating cholesterol).This person would have a transient decrease in the concentration of which type of hormone:
   A. Catecholamines
   B. Protein hormones
   C. steroids
   D. Iodothyronines
   E. Peptide hormones

4. Steroid hormones are large, lipid-soluble molecules derived from cholesterol. There are a variety of steroid hormones with different functions; they act on intracellular receptors. What is the function of glucocorticoids?
   A. Sodium and potassium homeostasis
   B. The formation of glucose and the breakdown of proteins and lipids
   C. Pregnancy and ovarian cycles
   D. Female sexual development and characteristics
   E. Male sexual development and characteristics

5. Pituitary glycoprotein hormones are heterodimers containing an α subunit and a hormone-specific &beta sub-unit. The glycoprotein hormones of the pituitary include: α subunit and a hormone-specific &beta sub-unit. The glycoprotein hormones of the pituitary include:
   A. Thyrotropin, growth hormone, and luteinizing hormone
   B. Human chorionic gonadotropin, thyrotropin, and follicle-stimulating hormone
   C. Prolactin, growth hormone, and adrenocorticotropin
   D. Follicle-stimulating hormone, luteinizing hormone, and thyrotropin
   E. Follicle-stimulating hormone, luteinizing hormone, and prolactin

6. ACTH has rapid, intermediate and prolonged effects on the functioning of the fascicular zone. Which of the following is a quick effects target?
   A. Adrenal hypertrophy
   B. Cortisol secretion
   C. StAR activation D. Expression of CYP21A2
   E. Expression of the LDL receptor

7. A 36-year-old man who appears dysmorphic presents to the Diabetic clinic. Upon closer inspection, he has a pronounced brow and jaw, spaces between his teeth, and large hands. What is the most likely cause of his diabetes?
   A. Phaeochromocytoma
   B. Thyrotoxicosis
   C. Haemochromatosis
   D. Acromegaly
   E. Cystic fibrosis

8. A 25-year-old man presents with constant thirst, polyuria and polydipsia. He is passing several litres of urine a day and is waking from sleep several times a night to pass urine. He feels very dehydrated despite drinking large quantities of water. He is otherwise fit and well, however he had transpendoidal surgery for a prolactin-secreting adenoma 4 weeks previously.Which condition does this patient most likely have?
   A. Phaeochromocytoma
   B. Addison's disease
   C. Diabetes mellitus
   D. Central diabetes insipidus
   E. Wilson's disease

9. A patient has polyuria and polydipsia, and urinary osmolality is 100 mOsm/kg H2O. Polyuria and polydipsia are not corrected by intravenous injection of ADH, and exogenous ADH also does not alter urinary osmolality.What is the most likely disorder in this patient?
   A. Syndrome of inappropriate ADH secretion
   B. Hyperaldosteronism
   C. Central diabetes insipidus
   D. Nephrogenic diabetes insipidus
   E. Nephrolithiasis

10. Which of the following groups of changes, compared to normal, would you expect to find in a patient with diabetes insipidus due to the absence of ADH secretion and who has free access to abundant drinking water? Plasma osmolarityNa conc. + in plasmaProt. conc. in plasma Urine volume Water ingestion Option 1↔↔↓↑↓Option 2↔↔↑↑↔Option 3↑↑↑↑↑Option 4↑↑↑↔↔Option 5↓↓↓↔↔
    A. Option 1 B. Option 2
    C. Option 3 D. Option 4
    E. Option 5

11. Postoperatively, patients are sometimes anuric due to increased circulating antidiuretic hormone. Which of the follow stimuli can cause the secretion of antidiuretic hormone?
    A. Hyperventilation
    B. Fall in blood pressure
    C. Increase in core body temperature
    D. Increase in intracranial pressure
    E. Infection

12. A patient has a myxedema. Which of the following groups of physiological changes would you expect? Cardiac output [RT3in plasma Plasma cholesterol A↑↑↑B↑↓↓C↓↑↓D↓↓↑E↓↓↓
    A. Option A
    B. Option B
    C. Option C
    D. Option D
    E. Option E

13. The thyroid gland secretes two hormones synthesized by the iodination of tyrosine. Which one of the following is a characteristic of thyroid hormones?
    A. Four mature molecules are released from thyroglobulin
    B. They are water soluble
    C. They can be conjugated in the liver to form cholesterol
    D. They enter the bile and then the intestine for elimination
    E. They have a short-half life

14. Which of the following hormones is synthesized from an iodinated tyrosine moiety in a large precursor molecule, has three iodide residues, is transported in the blood bound to plasma proteins and has a long half-life?
    A. Adrenaline
    B. Triiodothyronine
    C. Thyroid stimulating hormone
    D. T hyroxine
    E. Growth hormone

15. Over a period of several months, a patient has developed hyperpigmentation, hyperkalemia, and a tendency to lower blood sugar between meals. However, arterial blood pressure appears to be within the normal range. Which of the following conditions does the patient most likely have?
    A. Addison's disease
    B. Hypophysis adenoma
    C. Adrenal adenoma
    D. Panhypopituitarism
    E. Ectopic adenoma secretor of ACTH

16. In a patient with chronic excessive aldosterone secretion (i.e., primary aldosteronism), which of the following groups of conditions would you expect to find (compared to normal) under equilibrium conditions, assuming that electrolyte ingestion remains constant? Blood pressureExcretion rate of K+ in urineK conc.+ in plasmaPlasma renin conc.Na excretion rate+ in urine Option 1↑↑↓↓↓Option 2↑↔↓↓↔Option 3↑↑↓↓↔Option 4↔↑↔↔↔Option 5↓↔↑↑↔Option 6↓↓↑↔↓
    A. Option 1
    B. Option 2
    C. Option 3
    D. Option 4
    E. Option 5
    F. Option 6

17. A patient shows the following blood test values: Blood pH = 7.55 HCO3– in plasma = 40 mEq/L Plasma chloride concentration = 101 mEq/L Arterial pCO2 = 48 mmHg Plasma sodium = 150 mEq/LWhich is the most likely cause of their abnormal acid-base status?
    A. Pneumonia
    B. Conn syndrome
    C. Fanconi syndrome
    D. Chronic kidney disease
    E. Diarrhea

18. A 50-year-old man has had a history of hypertension for 3 years. He has received different medications without ever achieving a satisfactory control of his blood pressure. He's been off medication for the past six months. He suffers from fatigue and occasional muscle cramps. He has no family history of hypertension. He does not refer any other medical history of interest. The review shows a blood pressure of 168/104 mmHg. Blood test values indicate that the patient has primary hyperaldosteronism. Which of the following outcome groups would be most likely in this male with primary hyperaldosteronism? Extracellular fluid volumePlasma renin activityPlasma concentration of K+Option 1↑↑↑Option 2↑↓↑Option 3↑↓↓Option 4↑↑↓Option 5↓↓↓Option 6↓↑↓Option 7↓↑↑Option 8↓↓↑
    A. Option 1
    B. Option 2
    C. Option 3
    D. Option 4
    E. Option 5
    F. Option 6
    G. Option 7
    H. Option 8

19. Stress may have psychological or physical causes. Sepsis and trauma are physical causes, and when supporting sick patients, it is important to understand the metabolic changes that take place during stress. These occur in response to the secretion of cytokines and

classical hormones. What hormone changes occur in stress?

A. In severe hypoglycaemia, cortisol works in tandem with glucagon to amplify hepatic glycogenolysis
B. In chronic stress, plasma adrenaline levels rise in response to the need for glucose, and stimulate glycogen synthesis
C. Like glucagon, the action of cortisol leads to increases in blood glucose concentration, but has a much slower effect
D. Cortisol is secreted by the thyroid gland, controlled by the hypothalamic–pituitary axis
E. Adrenaline has a second glycogenolytic pathway, via β–adrenergic receptors

20. Cortisol may bind to the glycocorticosteroid receptor and the mineralcorticosteroid receptor. In distal nephron cells, one of the following phenomena prevents the binding of cortisol to the mineralcorticosteroid receptor:
A. Competitive inhibition by aldosterone
B. Conjugation with a glucuronide
C. Conversion to cortisone
D. Rapid excretion
E. Binding to chaperone proteins of thermal shock

21. Which of the following groups of physiological changes would you expect in a non-diabetic patient with Cushing's disease? [Aldosterone] in plasma [Cortisol] in plasma[Insulin] in plasma A↑↑↑ B↑↑↔ C↑↔↔ D↔↔↑ E↔↑↔ F .↔↑↑
A. Option A
B. Option B
C. Option C
D. Option D
E. Option E
F. Option F

22. Under the optical microscope the adrenal glands show cells arranged in vertical columns and surrounded by capillaries. These cells show lighter staining than the regions above and below. The upper region is characterized by the presence of pink cell balls surrounded by capillaries. What is the main hormone released by this adrenal layer?
A. Aldosterone
B. Cortisol
C. Dehydroepiandrosterone and androstenedione
D. Epinephrine
E. 11-Desoxicosticosterone

23. This is synthesized from the amino acid tyrosine, is water soluble and circulates freely in the blood weakly bound to albumin. It has a short half-life, is metabolized by monoamine oxidase and is not secreted by the hypothalamus.Which hormone best fits this description?
A. Adrenaline B. Triiodothyronine
C. Vasopressin D. Thyroxine
E. Dopamine

24. From the embryological point of view, the adrenal medulla is in reality only a sympathetic ganglion that has lost its postganglionic fibers and that, instead, directly secretes the adrenaline and noradrenaline hormones to the bloodstream. What substance stimulates the medulla to release these hormones?
A. Acetylcholine B. Dehydroepiandrosterone
C. Renin D. Oxytocin
E. Secretin

25. After his annual physical examination, a 55-year-old man is found to have a body mass index of 33 (above 30 = obese) and high blood pressure. Blood chemistry shows hyperlipemia, hypertriglyceridemia and hypercholesterolemia. In addition, the basal blood glucose concentration is 120 mg/dL (high). His doctor suspects type 2 diabetes and orders a glucose tolerance test. The patient drinks 75 g of glucose and then his blood glucose is measured at 2 o'clock. The glucose concentration at 2 h is 190 mg/dL (upper end of the glucose intolerance interval; the diagnosis of diabetes is equal to or greater than 200 mg/dL).The most likely reason for this patient's glucose intolerance is:
A. Autoimmune destruction of beta cells
B. Channel alteration from ATP-sensitive K+
C. Insulin resistance
D. Low leptin concentration
E. Alteration of GLUT2 function

26. Which of the following changes would you expect to find in a 12-year-old patient who has recently been diagnosed with type 1 diabetes mellitus and uncontrolled hyperglycemia (plasma glucose = 400 mg/dL)? Afferent arterial resistanceGFRThirst (water intake) Urine volumeOption 1↑↓↑↑Option 2↑↑↓↑Option 3↓↑↑↑Option 4↓↑↑↔Option 5↓↓↓↓Option 6↔↔↑↔
A. Option 1 B. Option 2 **C. Option 3**
D. Option 4 E. Option 5 F. Option 6

27. The prevalence of chronic renal failure is increasing. This is due to the increased prevalence of other diseases within the population. What is the most common cause of chronic renal failure?
A. Diabetes mellitus
B. Genetic problems
C. Glomerulonephritis
D. Hypertension
E. Medications

28. A large dose of insulin is given intravenously. Which of the following groups of hormonal changes in plasma would you expect in response to an insulin injection? Growth hormoneGlucagonEpinephrineA↑↓↔ B↔↑↑ C↑↑↑ D↓↑↑ E↓↓↔
A. Option A B. Option B **C. Option C**
D. Option D E. Option E

29. A 65-year-old woman reports a sharp, intense pain on her left side, radiating towards the pelvis. She also reports chronic musculoskeletal pain and indigestion. Radiology shows a kidney stone in the ureter. Blood biochemistry shows hypercalcemia, and urinary biochemistry shows hypercalciuria and hyperphosphaturia.An endocrine disruption

compatible with these findings is:

A. Infection of the digestive tract, which inhibits the absorption of calcium and phosphate

B. Adenoma of the parathyroid glands, which secretes an excessive amount of PTH

C. Hepatocellular carcinoma of the liver, resulting in overproduction of 25-hydroxyvitamin D

D. Medullary carcinoma of the thyroid, which secretes large amounts of calcitonin

E. Autoimmune destruction of the parathyroid glands

30. A 40-year-old woman comes to the emergency department with the femoral neck fractured. X-rays show widespread demineralization of bone in that area. The plasma ionic calcium concentration is significantly higher than normal, 12.2 mg %. Which of the following conditions is compatible with this presentation?

A. Osteoporosis

B. Rickets

C. Vitamin D deficiency

D. Hyperparathyroidism

E. Renal failure

31. A male eats a meal rich in Ca2. Which of the following effects would be an appropriate compensatory response to post-prandial changes in the plasma concentration of Ca2?

A. Increased secretion of calcitonin

B. Increased formation of 1,25-(OH)2D3

C. Increased osteoclastic activity

D. Increased renal resorption of Ca^{2+}

E. Increased osteocytic lysis

* * *

VIVA / SHORT QUESTION

1. What are the major endocrine glands?

Ans: Hypothalamus, Pituitary (anterior and posterior pituitaries), Thyroid, Adrenals (adrenal cortex and medulla), Parathyroid, Endocrine pancreas, Gonads (testis and ovary), Pineal gland

2. What are the hypothalamic hormones?

Ans: Thyrotropin releasing hormone, gonadotropin releasing hormone, corticotropin releasing hormone, growth hormone releasing hormone, prolactin releasing hormones, growth hormone inhibiting hormone (Somatostatin), and prolactin inhibiting hormones (Dopamine). Other hormones of hypothalamus are neuropeptide Y, orexins, MCH, ghrelin, MSH and CART.

3. What is the hypothalamo-hypophyseal tract?

Ans: The hypothalamus is connected separately and differently with anterior and posterior pituitaries. The connection with anterior pituitary is by means of blood vessels (portal-hypophyseal vessels) and with posterior pituitary is through the neurons (hypothalamo-hypophyseal tract).

4. What are the hormones of anterior pituitary?

Ans: Growth hormone (GH) or somatotropin, Thyroid-stimulating hormone (TSH) or thyrotropin, Adrenocorticotropic hormone (ACTH) or corticotropin, Follicle-stimulating hormone (FSH) or gonadotropin, Luteinizing hormone (LH) or gonadotropin, Prolactin

Other hormones are: β–lipotropin (β -LPH), α-melanocyte-stimulating hormone (α-MSH) and interleukins.

5. What are the factors that increase GH hormone secretion?

Ans: Hypoglycemia, Hyperaminoacidemia, Hormones: Estrogens, androgens, acetylcholine, serotonin and glucagon, Stress, Puberty, Stage IV sleep, Drugs: L-dopa, α receptor agonists, apomorphine, Enkephalins.

6. What are the factors that increase GH hormone secretion?

Ans: Increase in glucose and free fatty acid, Hormones: Cortisol, GH, medroxyprogesterone, REM sleep, Obesity.

7. What is the mechanism of action of GH hormone?

Ans: Activation of JAK-STAT pathway and through somatomedins (IGF-1 and IGF-2)

8. What are the actions of GH hormone?

Ans: 1. Stimulation of linear growth (Incorporation of proline into collagen and its conversion into hydroxyproline, Incorporation of sulfate into the proteoglycan chondroitin, Increased amino acid uptake and protein synthesis, and increased RNA and DNA synthesis in chondrocytes, Increase in size and number of chondrocytes, Dfferentiation of prechondrocytes to chondrocytes).

2. Increased total bone mass and mineral content of bone, increased osteoblastic activity.
3. Increase in the growth of skeletal muscle by increasing protein synthesis
4. Stimulation of growth of many visceral organs like liver, kidney, heart, pancreas, intestine
5. Increase in release of glucose from liver by facilitating hepatic neoglucogenesis, It decreases glucose uptake by skeletal muscle,
6. Lipolysis and increase in plasma level of FFA

9. What is acromegaly?

Ans: Acromegaly means enlargement of acral (peripheral) parts of the body. Hypersecretion of GH after the fusion of epiphysis results in acromegaly.

Features are enlargement of acral parts of the body, especially of hands and feet, prognathism (protrusion of lower jaw), acromegalic facies (overgrowth of malar, frontal and facial bones, increased amount body hair, osteoarthritis (due to skeletal changes), glucose intolerance, hirsutism, gynecomastia and lactation, and visual field changes (bitemporal hemianopia). Surgical removal of tumor is the best option to cure the disease.

10. What is acromegaly?
Ans: Hypersecretion of GH before fusion of epiphysis results in gigantism.
Features are abnormally tall, with giant stature. Surgical removal of tumor at the earliest cures the disease.

11. What is the function of prolactin?
Ans: To stimulate milk synthesis and secretion

12. What are the functions of ADH?
Ans: 1. Increases water reabsorption by acting on DCT and collecting duct of renal tubule.
2. Causes vasoconstriction.
3. Facilitates memory by acting as a neurotransmitter in memory areas of the brain.
4. Causes contraction of smooth muscles of spermatic cord.
5. Increases CRH release and therefore increases ACTH secretion.
6. Acts on area postrema to decrease cardiac output.
7. Causes glycogenolysis in liver.
8. Acts as a neurotransmitter in some areas of brain and spinal cord.

13. What is diabetes insipidus?
Ans: Diabetes insipidus is a syndrome due to deficiency of ADH. There is polyuria (large volume of dilute and tasteless urine and polydipsia.

14. What are the functions of Oxytocin?
Ans: Milk ejection reflex, Parturition reflex, contraction of smooth muscles of vas deferens that helps in propelling sperms towards the urethra.

15. What are the hormones secreted by thyroid gland?
Ans: T4 (thyroxine), T3 (triiodothyronine), RT3 (reverse-triiodothyronine), Calcitonin

16. What are the steps of thyroid hormone synthesis?
Ans: Five steps: i) Iodide trapping, ii) Conversion of iodide into iodine, iii) Thyroglobulin synthesis, iv) Coupling reaction, v) Proteolysis of thyroglobulin and secretion of thyroid hormones

17. What are the functions of thyroid hormone ?
Ans: i) Increase the basal metabolic rate by increasing oxygen consumption: increases food intake, body temperature and vitamins requirement.
ii) Development of the central nervous system: Growth of cerebral and cerebellar cortices, and basal ganglia, Proliferation of axons and branching of dendrites, Development of synaptic connections, Development of neurotransmitter systems in CNS, Myelination of neurons, General alertness and responsiveness to various stimuli, Speed and amplitude of stretch reflexes, Memory, learning and intellectual capacities
iii) Cardiovascular system: Increase heart rate and myocardial contractility, so increases the cardiac output. Increases HR by increasing the number and sensitivity of β receptors to catecholamines. Increases myocardial contractility by inducing myosin heavy chain (MHC) expression in the cardiac muscle. Increases systolic blood pressure and decreases diastolic blood pressure, so the pulse pressure increases.
iv) Essential for normal growth and musculo-skeletal maturation
v) Increases hepatic glucose output by inducing gluconeogenesis, Stimulates hepatic glycogenolysis. Increase absorption of glucose from intestine, Therefore, plasma glucose level increases.
vi) Stimulate lipolysis, promote proteolysis, enhance the motility GI tract

18. What are the features of hyperthyroidism?
Ans: Thyroid swelling, exophthalmos, periorbital edema, Increased BMR to as high as +100, increased body temperature, warm and moist skin, heat intolerance, sweating, fatigue, hyperactivity and irritability, nervousness, fine tremor, sinus tachycardia, systolic hypertension and increased pulse pressure, palpitation, weight loss inspite of hyperphagia, hyperdefecation, muscle weakness, loss of libido, and oligomenorrhea (in females), and gynecomastia (in males).

19. What is Grave's disease?
Ans: Grave's disease is an autoimmune disease that occurs due to development of autoantibodies against TSH receptors in which there is diffuse enlargement of thyroid gland, which is usually associated with exophthalmos.

20. What are the features of hypothyroidism?
Ans: BMR decreases to about –40, cold intolerance, cool extremities with dry coarse skin, loss of hair, weakness and easy-tiredness, bradycardia, puffy face, edematous hands and feet (myxedema), poor memory and inability to concentrate, constipation, weight gain inspite of poor appetite, thick and husky voice, alopecia, decreased reaction time of tendon reflexes (especially, delayed Achilles tendon reflex relaxation), menorrhagia (in females), galactorrhea and infertility, and plasma cholesterol is usually elevated.

21. What are the major hormones secreted from adrenal medulla?
Ans: Epinephrine, Norepinephrine, Dopamine.

22. What is fight or flight response?
Ans: At the time of emergency, sympathetic stimulation and catecholamines released from adrenal medulla increase cardiac output, promote blood flow to organs, increase ventilation, stimulate energy supply, relax the smooth muscle of GI tract and urinary system, and cause piloerection. All these effects are intended to either fight with the enemy or escape fast from the enemy to protect, called fight or flight response.

23. What are the hormones secreted from adrenal cortex?
Ans: i) Mineralocorticoids (Aldosterone, Deoxycorticosterone) – from Zona Glomerulosa
ii) Glucocorticoids (Cortisol, Corticosterone) - from Zona Fasciculata
iii) Sex steroids (Dehydroepiandrosterone, Androstenedione) - from Zona Reticularis

24. What are the functions of Cortisol?

Ans: i) Metabolism: Cortisol increases plasma glucose by hepatic gluconeogenesis, increases secretion of glycogenolytic hormones and decreases the utilization of glucose.
facilitates proteolysis, inhibits protein synthesis and causes lipolysis.
ii) CVS and blood: Increases myocardial performance, maintains vascular reactivity, causes eosinopenia, basopenia, lymphocytopenia, mild erythrocytosis and thrombocytosis
iii) Bone: Inhibits bone formation and facilitates bone resorption, inhibits collagen synthesis.
iv) Others: Has profound anti-inflammatory, anti-allergic actions and immunosuppressive effects, permissive actions.
v) GIT: Stimulates HCl secretion from parietal cells of the stomach

25. What are the permissive actions of Cortisol?

Ans:

1. Vasopressor and bronchodilator effects of catecholamines.
2. Calorigenic effects of glucagon and catecholamines.
3. Lipolytic effects of catecholamines.
4. Development of mammary gland during puberty, in females.
5. Development of hepatic enzyme systems during fetal life.
6. Surfactant synthesis in the fetal lung and maturation of lungs during intrauterine life.
7. Development of bacterial flora and enzyme systems in the intestine.

26. What are the fetures of Cushing's syndrome?

Ans: Due to hypersecretion of glucocorticoids, there is Centripetal obesity and overweight, Moon face, Hypertension, Hirsutism and amenorrhea, Reddish purple striae, Ecchymoses, Proximal myopathy, Poor wound healing, Hyperglycemia and glucose intolerance, Osteoporosis, Emotional changes, Hyperacidity, Thin and scraggly hairs

27. What are the fetures of Addison's Disease?

Ans: Due to hyposecretion of glucocorticoid, there is Loss of weight and easy fatigability, Pigmentation of skin, Hypotension, Anorexia, nausea and sometimes abdominal pain, Hyponatremia, hyperkalemia, Eosinophilia, Rapid hypoglycemia on fasting.

28. What are the functions of aldosterone?

Ans: Increase Na+ and water reabsorption and promote K+ and H+ excretion from the kidney. Thus, reabsorption of salt and water leads to ECF expansion.

29. What are the fetures of Conn's Syndrome?

Ans: Hypertension, muscle weakness and fatigue, and polyuria; Hypokalemia, hypernatremia and low renin in plasma, and metabolic alkalosis are usual laboratory findings.

30. What are the cells of pancreas and hormones secreted from it?

Ans: β cells (B cells): Insulin; α cells (A cells): Glucagon, δ cells (D cells): Somatostatin, F cells (PP cells): Pancreatic polypeptide.

31. What are the functions of Insulin?

Ans: i) On Glucose metabolism: Insulin increases glucose entry into the cell, stimulates glycolysis, promotes glycogen synthesis, inhibits hepatic glycogenolysis, inhibits gluconeogenesis.
ii) On lipid metabolism: Insulin stimulates entry of glucose into the adipose tissue and then is converted into α-glycerophosphate, promotes storage of fatty acids as triglycerides, inhibits lipolysis and decreases release of stored FFA, decreases the level of free fatty acids and ketoacids in the plasma.
iii) On Protein Metabolism: Insulin facilitates amino acid entry, promotes protein synthesis and inhibits proteolysis.
iv) Others: Insulin facilitates the rapid entry of K^+ into the cell by stimulating Na^+-K^+ ATPase, promotes growth

32. What are the types of diabetes mellitus?

Ans: Two types: Type-1 { Insulin dependent diabetes mellitus (IDDM)}, and Type-2 {non-insulin dependent diabetes mellitus (NIDDM)}.

i) Type-1 Diabetes Mellitus: Due to insulin deficiency, caused by autoimmune destruction of β-cells of pancreas. If one of the twins develops the disease the other twin has more chance of developing the disease. The disease usually starts early in childhood, and ketoacidosis is common. The disease is treated by insulin replacement.

ii) Type-2 Diabetes Mellitus: Due to insulin receptor resistance. The chance of identical twin developing the disease (concordance rate) is 100%. The disease usually starts late, in third or fourth decade of life. The patients are usually overweight and sedentary in their habit. Hyperosmolal coma is seen. Treated by Oral antidiabetic drugs.

33. What are the features of diabetes mellitus?

Ans: Polyphagia, polyuria, polydipsia, weight loss in spite of increased food intake, hyperglycemia, and glycosuria. If not treated, the disease leads to ketosis, acidosis, and coma. In chronic cases, there may be diabetic retinopathy, neuropathy and nephropathy.

34. What are the functions of parathyroid hormone?

Ans: The primary action of PTH is to increase the level of calcium and decrease the level of phosphate in the plasma, by acting on kidney, bone, and GIT.In the kidney, PTH increases the reabsorption of calcium, and decreases reabsorption of phosphate. In the bone, PTH increases bone resorption and mobilizes calcium and phosphates from bones into plasma. In the GIT, PTH increases absorption of calcium, through 1,25-dihydroxycholecalciferol.

35. What are the features of parathyroidectomy?

Ans: Hypocalcemic tetany. The features of tetany are:
i) Chvostek's sign: Quick contraction of facial muscles of the same side by tapping over the facial nerve at the angle of jaw.
ii) Trousseau's sign: Flexion at metacarpophalangeal joints with extension of interphalangeal joints.
iii) Carpopedal spasm: There is also spasm of muscles at the wrist joints (carpal spasm) and ankle joints.
iv) Laryngospasm, Hypocalcemia, Hyperphosphatemia.

36. What are the functions of calcitonin?

Ans: Calcitonin decreases the plasma calcium and phosphate level. It dereases bone resorption by inhibiting the osteoclastic activity. It decreases their reabsorption from kidney.

37. What are the functions of vitamin D?

Ans: Vitamin D increases plasma calcium and phosphate level by acting on intestine, kidney and bone. In the intestine, it facilitate absorption of calcium and phosphate. In the kidney, it increase their reabsorption. It stimulates bone resorption.

38. What are the features of vitamin D deficiency?

Ans: Deficiency of vitamin D causes rickets in children and osteomalacia in adults, due to decreased mineralization of bone causing reduced bone rigidity.

Features of Ricket: Bowing of the long bones of lower limbs and ricketic chest. The epiphyseal growth centers are affected.

Features of Osteomalacia: Bone pain, vertebral collapse, and fractures.

39. What is the hormone from the pineal gland?

Ans: Melatonin that coordinates the responses of body to the light-dark cycle, provides the skin colour.

SECTION IX- REPRODUCTIVE SYSTEM

MULTIPLE CHOICE QUESTIONS

1. By about 5 weeks of gestation, the embryonic Wolffian (mesonephric) and Müllerian (paramesonephric) ducts have the potential to develop into either a male or a female urogenital tract. Structures developed from the Müllerian (paramesonephric) ducts are usually absent in which of the following conditions?
   A. Adrenogenital syndrome (XX individuals with excessive secretion of androgens)
   B. Androgen insensitivity syndrome (testicular feminization)
   C. Normal people with XX sex chromosomes
   D. People with XXX sex chromosomes
   E. Turner's syndrome with sex chromosomes XO

2. During embryonic development, the gonads of the human embryo have the potential to become either testes or ovaries before 6 weeks. Which statement about the genetic control of the embryological development of the gonads is correct?
   A. A sex-determining region on the X chromosome (SRX) directs the primordial germ cells to develop into ovaries
   B. A sex-determining region on the Y chromosome (SRY) directs the primordial germ cells to develop into testes
   C. All structural genes necessary for developing the gonads are located on sex chromosomes
   D. Testosterone is essential for the development of testes
   E. XXY individuals may have both testes and ovaries

3. A 17-year-old girl has not had her first menstrual period (menarche) and has no signs of growth associated with puberty, breast development, or pubic hair growth. Her pediatrician suspects hypogonadism/puberty delay of some kind. A form of hypogonadism is associated with the loss of GnRH-producing neurons in the hypothalamus (Kallmann syndrome). This form of tertiary hypogonadism produces which of the following alterations?:
   A. Increases prolactin concentration
   B. Decreased TSH concentration
   C. Increased ACTH concentration
   D. Increased LH concentration
   E. Decreased FSH concentration

4. By about 5 weeks of gestation, the embryonic Wolffian (mesonephric) and Müllerian (paramesonephric) ducts have the potential to develop into either a male or a female urogenital tract.Which structure develops from the embryological Wolffian (mesonephric) system?
   A. Epididymis
   B. Ovaries
   C. Oviducts
   D. Penis
   E. Testes

5. The hypothalamic–pituitary–testicular axis regulates androgen secretion and spermatogenesis.Which statement about the regulation of androgen and spermatozoa synthesis is true?
   A. Follicle-stimulating hormone is essential for effective spermatogenesis B.Follicle-stimulating hormone is essential for the secretion of testosterone
   C. Inhibin enhances the release of follicle-stimulating hormone
   D. Luteinizing hormone is essential for the secretion of oestrogen
   E. Oestrogen is essential for effective spermatogenesis

6. The deficiency of which of the following hormones is likely to be causing infertility in a 34-year-old man after severe mumps?
   A. Oestrogen B. Insulin
   C. Parathyroid hormone **D. Testosterone**
   E. Erythropoietin

7. Ejaculation is controlled by a reflex arc involving several nerves and neurotransmitters. The final neurotransmitter of this arc, which directly stimulates the muscle contraction of the male reproductive system, is:
   A. Acetylcholine B. Nitric oxide C. Oxytocin
   D. Noradrenaline E. Somatostatin

8. The following hormone profile (low oestradiol, low progesterone, very high LH, very high FSH and undetectable hCG levels) is seen at which point in the menstrual cycle or phase of pregnancy listed below?
   A. Pregnancy third trimester
   B. Menstrual cycle day 14
   C. Menstrual cycle day 21
   D. Polycystic ovarian syndrome (PCOS)
   E. Post-menopause

9. The sequence of events in the ovaries (ovarian cycle) and the endometrium (menstrual cycle) are synchronized so that ovulation coincides with optimal conditions in the female reproductive tract for fertilization of the ovum and implantation. Which process occurs during the late luteal phase of the menstrual cycle?
   A. Sperm penetration into cervical mucus is enhanced
   B. Stromal atrophy occurs in the uterus
   C. The early morning basal body temperature is higher in luteal phase than in the follicular phase
   D. The cervix produces watery mucus under oestrogenic effect
   E. The number of progesterone receptors in the uterus decreases

10. On day 21 of a woman's reproductive cycle, how are the following hormones modified? Estradiol Progesterone FSHLH Activ in Inhibin A↑↓↓↓↓↑ B↑↑↓↓↓↑ C↓↑↓↓↓↑ D↑↑↑↓↑↓
    A. Option A **B. Option B**
    C. Option C D. Option D
    E. Option E

11. A dominant Graafian follicle releases the oocyte in response to an increase in luteinizing hormone at mid-cycle. After ovulation, the primary oocyte that has been released completes meiosis I and becomes a secondary haploid oocyte 23 (2n), with a cell lining called the zona pellucida. Where and when does the secondary oocyte complete meiosis II and become an oocyte 23 (1n)?
    A. In the uterus, before fertilization
    B. In the ampulla of the fallopian tube, in response to fertilization
    C. In the uterine cervix, before fertilization
    D. On the isthmus of the fallopian tube, 1 day after fertilization
    E. The secondary oocyte never completes meiosis II, nor is it fertilized by a spermatozoon.

12. A number of couples have difficulty in conceiving. Which of the following is true about infertility?
    A. Infertility is the inability of a couple to achieve a pregnancy after 3 months of unprotected intercourse
    B. Primary infertility refers to cases where the man has never fathered a child
    C. Secondary infertility is the inability of a couple to conceive after 4 years of unprotected intercourse
    D. The commonest cause of female infertility is diabetes
    E. Endometriosis causes infertility

13. The following hormone profile (very high progesterone levels, moderately high hCG, high human placental lactogen (hPL) and very high prolactin levels) are seen at which point in the menstrual cycle or phase of pregnancy listed below?
    A. Pregnancy third trimester
    B. Menstrual cycle day 14
    C. Menstrual cycle day 21
    D. Polycystic ovarian syndrome (PCOS)
    E. Post-menopause

14. During labour, pressure of the fetal head on the cervix stimulates the hypothalamus to release oxytocin, which acts on the uterine smooth muscle to increase the rate and force of contractions to expel the fetus.What is the positive feedback mechanism that causes the release of oxytocin?
    A. Adaption and change in parameter values acceptable as normal
    B. Amplification and self-perpetuation
    C. No response
    D. Significant response to return the variable to a steady state value lower than previously acceptable as normal
    E. The return of the variable to the normal steady state

15. After fertilization, the fertilized ovum enters the pre-embryo stage. Which of the following occurs in the fertilized ovum during the development of the pre-embryo?
    A. remains in the fallopian tube
    B. blastocysts secrete enzymes that digest the endometrium
    C. Migrates to the uterus and remains for 2–3 days before implantation
    D. stromal cells enlarge, to become the morula
    E. implantation occurs when levels of progesterone and oestrogen fall

16. A 24-year-old obese woman presents to her GP surgery for advice on contraception. She tells the GP that she is fit and well, but further questioning reveals that she is taking warfarin after developing a PE following a flight from Florida. The GP notes that her INR is low and she explains that she sometimes forgets to take her warfarin. She is not keen on barrier contraception as she previously fell pregnant whilst relying on it and had an abortion. She also admits to a needle phobia. She tells you that she would like children eventually, but perhaps in a year or two. What contraception would you recommend?
    A. Combined oral contraceptive pill
    B. Progesterone only pill
    C. Implanon
    D. Mirena IUCD
    E. Sterilization

VIVA / SHORT QUESTION

1. What is müllerian inhibiting substance (MIS) ? What are its functions?
   Ans: Also known as antimüllerian hormone or müllerian regression factor, MIS is a hormone secreted by the Sertoli cells of testis.
   Functions of MIS: i) In males, during early embryonic life, MIS inhibits development of female gonads by promoting regression of müllerian duct. Therefore, it helps in male gonadal development.
   ii) During fetal life in males, it helps in testicular descent.
   iii) In both sexes, it helps in maturation of germ cells.

2. What is Turner's syndrome (gonadal or ovarian dysgenesis)?
   Ans: The chromosomal pattern is 44 XO (44 autosomes and one X chromosome, so total 45 chromosomes). Diminished sexual development, dwarfism, and webbing of the neck with no gonadal tissue or rudimentary gonads, primary amenorrhea, no sexual maturation at puberty.

3. What is Klinefelter's syndrome (seminiferous tubule dysgenesis)?
   Ans: Primary hypogonadism and infertility in male (feminine features in an apparent male with small testes). The patient is genetically female, with 47 XXY (44 autosomes + XX sex chromosomes + one extra Y chromosome), has male genitalia and at puberty male characteristics develop due to adequate testosterone. Infertility results as seminiferous tubules are not properly developed. Mental retardation is present. It is the most common sex chromosome abnormality.

4. What is testicular feminization syndrome?
   Ans: The patients are genetic males (XY karyotype), but appear normal female externally. The gonads are testis; with immature seminiferous tubules, spermatogenesis does not occur. Though the external genitalia are of female type, there is no development of uterus. The vagina ends in a blind pouch. At puberty though breasts develop normally, the growth of pubic and axillary hairs is scanty. There is primary amenorrhea.

5. What is superfemales?
   Ans: The karyotype is XXX. It is not associated with any characteristic abnormalities and therefore remains undetected.

6. What is true hermaphroditism?
   Ans: This is a rare condition in which both testes and ovaries are present. Sometimes, ovary is present on one side and the testis on the opposite side. Both male and female sex differentiations occur with the development of combined female and male external and internal genitalia. Usually, the karyotype pattern is 46 XX-XY.

7. What is blood-testis barrier?
   Ans: The tight junction between Sertoli cells near the basal lamina forms the blood-testis barrier (BTB), which does not allow substances from interstitial space and blood to pass through them except steroids and few proteins.

8. What are the functions of Sertoli cells?
   Ans: 1. Provide structural support and nutrition for germ development
   2. Phagocytosis of residual bodies and damaged germ cells from the seminiferous tubules.
   3. Nourishment and growth of spermatids
   4. Formation of tubular fluid of seminiferous tubule
   5. Support spermiation: Help in detachment of mature sperms from Sertoli cells by producing plasminogen activator that forms plasmin.
   6. Have receptors for FSH and testosterone.
   7. Hormone secretion: Inhibin, Activin, Follistatin, Müllerian regression substance, Estrogens
   8. Secretion of androgen binding proteins (ABP) and H-Y antigen
   9. Forms Blood-testis barrier

9. What are the functions of blood-testis barrier?
   Ans: BTB protects germ cells in the seminiferous tubules from harmful elements in blood. BTB prevents the antigenic elements produced by germ cells to escape into circulation from tubule and thus, prevents autoimmune reactions. BTB maintains the composition of the fluid in the lumen of seminiferous tubules. BTB maintains higher osmolality of luminal content of the seminiferous tubules, which favours the osmotic movement of fluid into the tubular lumen.

10. What are the functions of Testis?
    Ans: Spermatogenesis, Secretion of Testosterone, activin, inhibin and follistatin

11. What are the steps of spermatogenesis?
    Ans: Spermatogonium undergoes mitosis to produce primary spermatocytes that undergo two meiotic divisions to form spermatids. Spermatids, by the process of spermiogenesis become mature spermatozoa.

12. What are the factors regulating spermatogenesis?
    Ans: i) Hormonal Factors: Androgen, estrogen, LH and FSH. Androgens stimulate spermatogenesis. Estrogen concentrates the fluid in the rete testis by facilitating fluid reabsorption. LH helps in spermatogenesis by producing a high local concentration of androgen. FSH maintains gametogenic functions of testis.
    ii) Temperature of scrotum: Spermatogenesis best occurs at 30 to 35°C.

13. What are the hormones secreted by testis?
    Ans: Testosterone, androstenedione, dihydrotestosterone, inhibin, activin, follistatin and Estrogen

14. What are the physiological actions of Testosterone?
    Ans: It stimulates spermatogenesis, promotes growth of male reproductive system and causes development of secondary sex characters, helps in descent of testis into scrotum, increases growth and development of bones and muscles, inhibits LH and FSH secretion from anterior pituitary, and stimulates erythropoiesis.

15. What is Cryptorchidism?
Ans: The failure of migration of testis from abdominal cavity into the scrotum during fetal development is called undescended testis or cryptorchidism. The usual site of undescended testis is inguinal rings.

16. What is corpus luteum?
Ans: After ovulation, the ruptured follicle is quickly filled with blood, called corpus hemorrhagicum. Then, the cells lining the follicle rapidly proliferate to replace blood with luteal cells that are rich in lipid. Now, the follicle is called corpus luteum.

17. What are the functions of corpus luteum?
Ans: i) Secretes hormones progesterone, estrogen, androgen and inhibin A.
ii) Provides endocrinal environment for implantation of fertilized ovum.
iii) Maintains the early part of pregnancy by secreting progesterone.

18. What are the indicators of ovulation?
Ans:
1. Rise in of basal body temperature during ovulation by about 0.5°C due to the influence of progesterone.
2. Fleeting lower abdominal pain (Mittelschmerz) as with ovulation, bleeding occurs into the antrum of the follicle that causes peritoneal irritation and produces fleeting (short-lived) lower abdominal pain.
3. Vaginal discharge (spotting)
4. Spinnbarkeit: Due to estrogen, uterine mucous is thinnest at the time of ovulation and its elasticity is maximal. Thus, a drop of cervical mucous can be stretched to as long as 10 cm or more like a thread. This elastic nature of the mucous is called spinnbarkeit.
5. Fern test: Under the effect of estrogen, the cervical mucous before ovulation forms an arborizing fern like pattern, when the mucous is spread on a slide.
6. Laparoscopic observation: Demonstrating ovum in the abdominal cavity by laparoscopy 7. Demonstration of LH peak

19. What is ovulation cascade?
Ans: When rise in BBT is associated with mittelschmerz and spotting, they are collectively called as ovulation cascade.

20. What are the phases of menstrual cycle?
Ans: Two phases: follicular phase and luteal phases
Follicular Phase (1–14 days): This is the period from the onset of bleeding to the day of ovulation. It includes the menstrual bleeding phase (1-5 days), and the proliferative phase Follicular phase is also called preovulatory phase. Increaed Estrogen causes proliferation of the uterine endometrium. Ovulation occurs on the 14th day.
Luteal Phase (15 to 28 days): Between ovulation and the onset of the next menstrual bleeding, also called postovulatory phase. Corpus luteum is formed in the ovary. Increased Prgesterone secretion makes the uterine endometrium glandular, vascular and secretory.

21. What are the uterine changes during Follicular phase of menstrual cycle?
Ans: The uterine endometrium undergoes hyperplasia and hypertrophy and increases in size and thickness. The endometrial glands lengthen and glands are drawn out and there is formation of more number of veins and spiral arteries in the endometrium. Myometrial excitability increases. Under the effects of estrogen, volume of cervical mucous, its alkalinity and elasticity increases.

22. What are the uterine changes during Luteal phase of menstrual cycle?
Ans: Due to the effects of progesterone, the uterine glands become coiled and tortuous and secrete mucous and fluid. The vascularity increases and the spiral arteries become tortuous, the endometrium becomes edematous and thick. Endometrial veins form venous lakes and anastomoses Myometrial excitability decreases. The cervical mucous becomes thick and its elasticity decreases. Towards later part, foci of necrosis appear, necrotic areas coalesce and endometrium starts sloughing at the end of secretory phase that heralds the onset of bleeding.

23. What are the hormones from ovary?
Ans: Ovary secretes estrogens, progesterone, inhibins and relaxin

24. What are the functions of Estrogen?
Ans: i) Estrogen promotes growth of ovary and ovarian follicles, stimulates smooth muscle contraction of fallopian tubes, increases uterine size, causes proliferation of uterine endometrium, increases uterine blood flow, increases the activity and excitability of uterine muscle, cervical mucus becomes abundant, clear, and watery.
ii) On Breast: Estrogen causes breast enlargement during puberty. It also causes pigmentation of the areola.
iii) Development of secondary sexual characteristics.
iv) On endocrine organs: Estrogen inhibits LH, FSH secretion, stimulates prolactin secretion.
v) On musculoskeletal system: Estrogen stimulates bone growth, prevents osteoclastic activity, causes epiphyseal closure, hence causes cessation of longitudinal growth of bone and therefore, determines the height of the female.
v) On Lipid Profile: Estrogen prevents atherosclerosis.
vi) On sebaceous secretion & skin: Estrogen promotes more fluid secretions, inhibits the formation of acne.

25. What are the functions of Progesterone?
Ans: Progesterone causes relaxation of uterine smooth muscles inhibits uterine myometrial contractions, It causes the cervical mucus to become thick and sticky. It promotes growth of the glandular tissue of the breast. Increases body temperature (approximately 0.5°C) immediately after ovulation. It decreases LH secretion, stimulates respiration, causes vasodilation (Therefore, diastolic pressure decreases in pregnancy).

26. What are the hormones secreted from Placenta?
Ans: Human chorionic gonadotropin (hCG), Human chorionic somatotropin (hCS), Relaxin, Progesterone, Estrogen

27. What are the mechanisms of action of Oral contraceptive pills?

Ans: Oral contraceptives pills containing estrogen and progesterone inhibit pituitary gonadotropin release, thereby prevent ovulation. Progesterone only pill affects the composition of the cervical mucus, reducing the ability of the sperm to pass through the cervix, and inhibit the estrogen-induced proliferation of the endometrium, making it inhospitable for implantation.

28. What are the hormones secreted from placenta?

Ans:

i) Changes in blood: There is rapid and significant increase in total blood volume, Red cell count increases and increase in procoagulant activity.

iii) Changes in cardiovascular system: Increase in cardiac output due to increase in both stroke volume and heart rate, thus systolic pressure increases. Diastolic pressure falls due to the vasodilation effect of progesterone. Blood flow increases in uterine, renal, mammary and cutaneous vascular bed.

iv) Increase in minute ventilation, renal blood flow, decrease in GI motility, increase in body weight .

29. What are the mechanisms of action of IUD?

Ans:

i) Interfere with the endometrial preparation for acceptance of the blastocyst. Thus, implantation is prevented.

ii) They also act as foreign body in the uterine cavity causing cellular and biochemical changes in the endometrium and the uterine fluid that impair the viability of the gamete.

Iii) Copper facilitates cellular reaction in endometrium, composition of cervical mucus, impairs sperm motility and impairs capacitation of sperm.

iv) Hormone releasing devices increase the viscosity of cervical mucus by releasing progesterone. They make mucous thick, so that sperm can not enter uterus. They also make the endometrium unfavorable for implantation.

SECTION X- RENAL SYSTEM

MULTIPLE CHOICE QUESTIONS

1. Urine is normally formed continuously by the kidneys and stored in the bladder.Which of the following is a characteristic of congenital vesico-ureteric reflux?
   A. Presents more often in boys than girls
   B. Due to an embryonic developmental defect in the renal pelvis
   C. Presents as recurrent urinary tract infections in children
   D. Intermittent antibiotics to treat urinary tract infection (UTI) is the treatment of choice
   E. May cause nephritic syndrome

2. Compared to normal, which of the following groups of changes would you expect to find in a patient with acute proximal tubular necrosis and a significant decrease in the reabsorption of proximal tubular sodium chloride? Sodium reabsorption in the loop of HenleGFRAfferent arteriolar resistance Renal blood flow Option 1↑↓↑↓ Option 2 ↑↑↑↑ Option 3 ↓↑↓↑ Option 4↓↑↑↓ Option 5↔↓↑↓
   A. Option 1
   B. Option 2
   C. Option 3
   D. Option 4
   E. Option 5

3. Hyponatremia can sometimes be seen in people whose ECF volume has decreased by more than 10%.Which of the following factors contributes to the onset of hyponatremia in this situation?
   A. Decreased ADH concentration
   B. Elevation of the concentration of natriuretic peptides
   C. Increased excretion of Na+ by the kidneys
   D. Reduced excretion of solute-free water by the kidneys
   E. Appearance of a positive Na^+ balance

4. A 25-year-old man is brought into the Emergency Department in the middle of the night with abdominal pain and vomiting after a night out with friends. Whilst in the Department a BM was performed giving a blood glucose reading of 23 mmol/L. An arterial blood gas was performed giving a reading of:

   pH- 7.35 (normal range pH 7.35–7.45)
   PaCO2-3 kPa (normal range 4.7–6 kPa)
   Bicarbonate- 12 mmol/L (normal range 22–26 mmol/L)
   PaO2-11 kPa (normal range 11.3–12.6 kPa)

   What does his arterial blood gas read?
   A. Metabolic alkalosis
   B. Metabolic acidosis
   C. Compensated metabolic acidosis
   D. Respiratory alkalosis
   E. Respiratory acidosis

5. A 60-year-old woman arrives at the Emergency Department with shortness of breath. An arterial blood gas test is performed. Po2 75 mmHg (normal: 75 to 100 mmHg) Pco2 58 mmHg (normal: 33 to 44 mmHg) [HCO3-] 24 mEq/L (normal: 22 to 28 mEq/L) pH 7.24 (normal: 7.35 to 7.45) What is this woman's acid-base disorder?
   A. Metabolic acidosis
   B. Metabolic alkalosis
   C. Acute respiratory acidosis
   D. Acute respiratory alkalosis
   E. Chronic respiratory acidosis

6. A 6-year-old boy is treated in the emergency department with fever, abdominal cramps and diarrhea. His arterial blood gas shows the following: pH 7.28 (normal: 7.35 to 7.45) Pco2 24 mmHg (normal: 33 to 44 mmHg) [HCO3-] 11 mEq/L (normal: 22 to 28 mEq/L) What is the acid-base disorder?
   A. Metabolic acidosis with respiratory compensation
   B. Metabolic acidosis with respiratory acidosis
   C. Acute respiratory acidosis
   D. Chronic respiratory acidosis
   E. All of the above answers are false

7. Which of the following factors would tend to cause hyperkalemia by shifting potassium from the intracellular fluid to the extracellular fluid?
   A. Excess aldosterone
   B. Acidosis
   C. Beta adrenergic stimulation
   D. Increased insulin levels
   E. Decreased extracellular fluid osmolality

8. Match the patient with the correct set of blood values from the table. The same values can be used for more than one patient. Patient pH HCO3(mmol/l) pCO2(mmHg) Na+(mmol/l) Cl−(mmol/l) A 7,07 14 50 144 102 B 7,29 14 30 143 117 C 7,25 12 28 142 102 D 7,52 38 48 146 100 E 7,66 22 20 143 111 Which patient overdosed on acetylsalicylic acid and emphysema?
   A. Option A
   B. Option B
   C. Option C
   D. Option D
   E. Option E

9. Match the patient with the correct set of blood values from the table. The same values can be used for more than one patient. Patient pH HCO3(mmol/l) pCO2(mmHg) Na+(mmol/l) Cl−(mmol/l) A 7,07 14 50 144 102 B 7,29 14 30 143 117 C 7,25 12 28 142 102 D 7,52 38 48 146 100 E 7,66 22 20 143 111 Which patient has renal tubular acidosis?
   A. Option A **B. Option B** C. Option C
   D. Option D E. Option E

10. A woman suffers from peptic ulceration and takes aluminium hydroxide tablets regularly to relieve her symptoms. She collapses and is taken to the Emergency Department, where she is found to have a tissue pH of 7.49 (normal range pH is 7.35–7.45). What is the probable cause of her metabolic alkalosis?
   A. Excessive loss of bicarbonate ions
   B. An inability of the kidneys to excrete hydrogen ions
   C. Excessive use of antacid tablets
   D. Consumption of excessive amounts of water
   E. Hyperventilation

11. Maintenance of blood pH is a coordinated activity carried out by the liver, kidneys and lungs. One of the mechanisms for acid–base homeostasis uses the products of amino acid metabolism. Which one of the following is part of amino acids metabolism and linked to metabolic acidosis?
   A. The bicarbonate (HCO^{3-}) derived from the peripheral oxidation of amino acid skeletons is consumed
   B. Glutaminase is down-regulated, leading to an increase in blood ammonium ion (NH^{4+})
   C. Ammonium ion (NH^{4+}) accumulates in the blood
   D. Urine is more alkaline than blood (pH 7.4), so a pH gradient is established between urine and blood
   E. Urinary ammonium ion (NH^{4+}) excretion decreases

12. A 65-year-old man has chronic kidney failure. What are the expected changes in serum concentrations of Ca^{++}, Pi and calcitriol?
   A. Decrease in [Ca^{++}], increase in [Pi] and decrease in [calcitriol]
   B. Increase in [Ca^{++}] increase in [Pi] and increase in [calcitriol]
   C. Increase in [Ca^{++}], decrease in [Pi] and decrease in [calcitriol]
   D. Decrease in [Ca^{++}], decrease in [Pi] and decrease in [calcitriol]
   E. Increase in [Ca^{++}], increase in [Pi] and decrease in [calcitriol]

13. A patient with severe dizziness secondary to an inner ear infection suffers from a prolonged episode of vomiting. There is a high probability of systemic symptoms related to reduced plasma concentration of one of the following electrolytes, which one?
   A. HCO^{3-}
   B. Cl^{-}
   C. Na^{+}
   D. H^{+}
   E. K^{+}

14. 3.A healthy 55-year-old man goes to the doctor for a check-up. During physical examination, he shows a blood pressure of 170/98 mmHg. Other tests suggest renovascular hypertension due to left renal artery stenosis. Which of the following groups of results would be most likely in this male with renovascular hypertension? Total peripheral resistance Plasma renin Aldosterone Option 1 ↑ ↑ ↑ Option 2 ↑ ↓ ↑ Option 3 ↑ ↓ ↓ Option 4 ↑ ↑ ↓ Option 5 ↓ ↓ ↓ Option 6 ↓ ↑ ↓ Option 7 ↓ ↑ ↑ Option 8 ↓ ↓ ↑
   A. Option 1
   B. Option 2
   C. Option 3
   D. Option 4
   E. Option 5
   F. Option 6
   G. Option 7
   H. Option 8

VIVA / SHORT QUESTION

1. What are the functions of kidney?
Ans: Urine formation and excretion of waste products, Regulation of ECF volume, Regulation of blood pressure, Regulation of electrolyte composition of body fluids, Acid-base balance, Regulation of plasma osmolality, Regulation of erythropoiesis, Endocrine functions, Gluconeogenesis:

2. What are the differences between cortical and juxtamedullary nephrons?

	Cortical nephrons	Juxtamedullary nephrons
1. Location of renal corpuscle	In the superficial region of cortex	In the juxtamedullary region of the cortex
2. Number	85% of total	15% of total
3. Length of LOH	Shorter	Longer
4. Length of thin limb of LOH	Shorter, and thin ascending limb is almost absent	Longer, and thin limb has ascending & descending parts
5. Size of glomerulus	Usually small	Usually large
6. Tubular function	Filtration & reabsorption	Filtration, reabsorption, & creation of medullary osmolar gradient
7. Rate of filtration	Slow	High
8. Efferent arteriole	Forms peritubular capillaries.	Forms peritubular capillaries and vasa recta.
9. Vasa recta	Absent	Present, dipping into medulla
10. Efficiency in concentrating urine	Less	More
11. Renin content	More	Less
12. Main function	Urine formation & excretion of waste products	Urine concentration

3. What is juxtaglomerular apparatus?
Ans: The juxtaglomerular apparatus is formed by macula densa of the thick ascending limb of LOH, Juxtaglomerular cells (the modified muscle cells mainly of afferent arterioles), and Lacis cells (extraglomerular mesangial cells).

4. What is the function of juxtaglomerular apparatus?
Ans: JG cells secrete renin that activates renin-angiotensin system. Macula densa cells act as sensor that detects the change in rate of flow and volume of flow in the tubule, and composition of tubular fluid. Lacis cells secrete renin and erythropoietin.

5. Define Glomerular filtration rate (GFR)?
Ans: GFR is defined as the amount of filtrate formed by glomerular filtering membrane of both the kidneys in a unit time. Normally, it is 125 ml/min (7.5 L/h or 180 L/day).

6. What are the factors affecting GFR?
Ans:
   1. Change in renal blood flow: Increased blood flow to kidney increases GFR.
   2. Glomerular capillary hydrostatic pressure: Increased hydrostatic pressure in glomerular capillary increases GFR.
   3. Capsular hydrostatic pressure: Increased hydrostatic pressure in the Bowman's capsule and tubule decreases GFR.
   4. Oncotic pressure: Increased oncotic pressure in glomerular capillaries due to plasma proteins decreases GFR.
   5. Glomerular capillary permeability: Increased glomerular capillary permeability increases GFR.
   6. Effective filtration surface area: Increased size of filtration area increases GFR.
   7. Size, shape and electrical charge of the macromolecules.

7. What is tubuloglomerular feedback?
Ans: Increased renal arterial pressure increases pressure in the glomerular capillaries. This increases GFR and flow of fluid in the tubule, which is sensed by macula densa cells. Tubular cells provide signal to the glomerular apparatus that causes afferent arteriolar constriction to decrease GFR and bring it back to normal and maintain the constancy of load delivered to the tubule. This is called tubuloglomerular feedback.

8. What is glomerulotubular balance?
Ans: Normally, a constant fraction of filtered solute is reabsorbed by the proximal tubule. Increase in GFR increases the load of solutes, especially of Na^+ in the tubular fluid. This increases reabsorption of Na^+ from the proximal tubule. This is called glomerulotubular balance.

9. What is transport maximum for glucose (Tm_G)?
Ans: The maximum amount of glucose that can be transported from the tubular lumen into the renal tubular epithelium is known as transport maximum for glucose. TmG depends on the rate of glucose filtered into the tubule, which is calculated as plasma glucose concentration × GFR.
For e.g. when plasma glucose concentration is 80 mg/dL and GFR is 125mL/min, the rate of glucose filtered is 100 mg/min (80 × 125). The Tm_G is 375 mg/min in males and 300 mg/min in females. When Tm_G is exceeded, the glucose appears in urine.

10. What is renal splay?
Ans: The renal threshold is the TmG divided by GFR. When TmG is 375 mg/min and the GFR is 125mL/min, the renal threshold should be about 300 mg/dL. However, the actual renal threshold is about 200 mg/dL in arterial plasma and 180 mg/dL in venous plasma. Therefore, when the graph of TmG is plotted, the actual curve deviates from the ideal curve. This deviation is called renal splay. The splay is due to two reasons: TmG is not same in all the tubules, and amount of glucose removed from each tubule is not complete even when the amount filtered is below the TmG.

11. What is a countercurrent mechanism?

Ans: A countercurrent mechanism requires three conditions to operate:

1. There should be two tubes (inflow and outflow tubes) that should run parallel to each other.
2. The movement of fluid in one tube should be in opposite direction to the other.
3. The tubes should be in close proximity to each other and should be selectively permeable.

12. What is the countercurrent system in kidney?

Ans: Loop of Henle (LOH) acts as countercurrent multiplier and vasa recta as countercurrent exchanger. In LOH, fluid flows deep into the medulla along the descending limb and from medulla into the cortex along the ascending limb. The descending and ascending limbs for their selective permeabilities for water and solutes, establish an osmotic gradient in the medulla.

In vasa recta, blood flows in opposite direction in descending and ascending vessels during which water and solutes are exchanged passively between capillary blood vessels. This passive exchange in vasa recta maintains the osmotic gradient.

Collecting duct is juxtaposed to LOH and vasa recta, and acts as an osmotic equilibrating device.

13. What is aquaporin?

Ans: Aquaporins are water channels made up of proteins that facilitate transport of water across the membrane of tubular epithelial cells of kidney. Aquaporin-1 is found proximal tubule and loop of Henle, and aquaporin-2 in the collecting duct. In the collecting duct, ADH binds with V2 receptor and stimulates the formation and insertion of vesicle containing aquaporin-2 on luminal surface of the epithelial cells that increases water permeability.

14. What is osmotic diuresis?

Ans: The increased excretion of water by increased concentration of osmotically active particles in the tubular fluid is called as osmotic diuresis. In diabetes mellitus, increased tubular glucose load causes osmotic diuresis.

15. What is a diuretic, give examples?

Ans: Diuretics are substances that promote diuresis (increased excretion of water in urine).

Loop Diuretics (Furosemide and ethacrynic acid); Aldosterone Antagonists (Spironolactone); Thiazide Diuretics (chlorothiazide), Carbonic Anhydrase Inhibitors (acetazolamide), Xanthines (caffeine and theophylline), Osmotically active Substances (mannitol and glucose), Ethanol, Acidifying Salts (calcium and ammonium chloride), Vasopressin Antagonists.

16. What are the factors contributing to acidification of urine?

Ans: Renal acid excretion, Renal bicarbonate reabsorption, Acid-base status of the body, Hormonal factors.

17. What is clearance?

Ans: Clearance is defined as the quantity of blood or plasma cleared of a substance for unit time. This is expressed as ml per minute. It is calculated by using the formula, $C = (U \times V) \div P$, where U = concentration of the substance in urine; P = concentration of the substance in plasma or serum and, V = the ml of urine excreted per minute. The value is expressed as ml/minute. inulin clearance test is the standard test for measurement of GFR.

SECTION XI- NEUROPHYSIOLOGY

MULTIPLE CHOICE QUESTIONS

1. 1.Neurulation is the process in which the embryonic nervous system is organized and begins as early as day 16 after fertilization. Which one of the following is a feature of neural tube defects (spina bifida)?
   A. Alpha-fetoprotein level decreases in the amniotic fluid
   B. Defects in primary neurulation closure of the anterior end of the embryonic neural tube result in spina bifida
   C. Failure of the embryonic neural tube to close posteriorly causes anencephaly
   D. A protective effect of vitamin B12 against the development of neural tube defects is well recognized
   E. Spina bifida is very often associated with hydrocephalus

2. Axons are covered in a myelin sheath. Which of the following options best describes myelination?
   A. It is the function of microglial cells
   B. Increases the speed of nerve conduction
   C. Occurs in almost all nerve cells in the brain
   D. Is usually accompanied by deletion of calcium channels
   E. Never takes place in patients with multiple sclerosis

3. The trigeminal nerve (cranial V) is mainly sensory, but has motor fibres. Which of the following is true of the mandibular division of the trigeminal nerve?
   A. Originates from the trochlear ganglion in the petrous temporal bone
   B. Exits the skull base through the foramen rotundum
   C. Innervates the tip of the nose
   D. Mediates the jaw jerk
   E. Supplies the teeth and gums of the upper jaw

4. The «kiss and run» mechanism that enables vesicle recycling is of the greatest importance to keep the synaptic transmission in:
   A. An axon with a high discharge frequency and small presynaptic terminals
   B. The neuromuscular junction
   C. A large synapse in the CNS
   D. A presynaptic terminal with a low release probability
   E. All of the above answers are false

5. By means of which of the following circuits is it possible to enhance the contrast of the signal in the different types of neural circuits?
   A. A divergent circuit
   B. A convergent circuit
   C. A reverberant circuit
   D. A circuit with lateral inhibition
   E. A circuit with collateral activation

6. For a sensitive nerve fiber that is connected to a free nerve termination located in the left hand, the synaptic connection with the next neuron in the appropriate sensory pathway is located in:
   A. The nucleus of the right dorsal column
   B. The dorsal horn on the right side of the spinal cord
   C. The core of the left dorsal column
   D. The dorsal horn on the left side of the spinal cord
   E. The nucleus of the left anterolateral fascicule

7. Targets for neural signalling are receptors. Sensory receptors convert the energy of a stimulus into a change in membrane potential (receptor potential) that travels along the nerve fibre. This is known as transduction. What is the physiological receptor for proprioception?
   A. Cochlea hair cells
   B. Muscle and joint mechanoreceptors
   C. Skin mechanoreceptors
   D. Thermoreceptors
   E. Vestibular hair cells

8. Photoreceptors are the light responsive elements and lie in close contact with the retinal pigmented epithelium. Which of the following mediates light adaptation in vertebrate photoreceptors?
   A. Rising cyclic AMP
   B. Falling calcium
   C. Rising cyclic GMP
   D. Falling chloride
   E. Rising transducin

9. Mechanoreceptors in the skin respond to mechanical stimuli that give rise to the sensations of touch, pressure, vibration, tickle and stretch.Which of the options below is the principal afferent pathway for conscious experience of mechanoreceptor sensation for limbs, trunk and posterior third of the head?
   A. Corticothalamic
   B. Dorsal column – medial lemniscus pathway
   C. Mesocortical pathway
   D. Mesolimbic pathway
   E. Nigrostriatal pathway

10. Mechanoreceptors in the skin respond to mechanical stress. The two main afferent pathways for conscious experience of mechanoreceptor sensation are the dorsal column-medial lemniscus pathway and the trigeminal lemniscus pathway. Which of the following statements about the dorsal column–medial lemniscal pathway is true?
    A. The cell bodies of the first-order neurons lie in the anterior root ganglia in the spinal cord
    B. The first-order neurons cross the midline in the spinal cord a few spinal segments above
    C. The cell bodies of the second-order neurons lie in the nuclei gracilis and cuneatus in the dorsal column
    D. The second-order neuron does not cross the midline
    E. The third-order neuron projects from the hypothalamus to the sensory cortex

11. The spinothalamic tract and the dorsal column–medial lemniscus pathways are both sensory pathways.Which of the following are similarities in the spinothalamic tract and the dorsal column–medial lemniscal pathways?
    A. Both consist of two-order sets of neurones
    B. The second-order neurones cross over in both pathways
    C. Both pathways cross over in the spinal cord
    D. The third-order neurones project from the hypothalamus to the cerebral cortex
    E. The representations of different parts of the body in the motor cortex are similar

12. In a sensitive nerve fiber that is connected to the Paccini corpuscle located on the palmar surface of the right hand, the synaptic connection with the next neuron of your appropriate sensory pathway is located in:
    A. The nucleus of the right dorsal column
    B. The core of the left dorsal column
    C. The dorsal horn on the right side of the spinal cord
    D. The dorsal horn on the left side of the spinal cord
    E. The nucleus of the left anterolateral fascicule

13. The second neuron of the appropriate sensory pathway connecting a Meissner corpuscle in the palm of the left hand with the somatosensory cortex travels in:
    A. The contralateral lateral lemniscus
    B. The anterolateral homolateral spine
    C. The medial homolateral lemniscus
    D. The contralateral medial lemniscus
    E. The contralateral anterolateral spine

14. The raphe nuclei are a cluster of neurones in the brainstem near the midline. Serotonin (5-hydroxytryptamine, 5-HT) secreting neurones are located there. What is the role of the raphe nuclei?
    A. Cardiovascular and thermoregulatory and homeostasis
    B. Cortical modulation
    C. Pain perception
    D. Regulation of cerebral blood flow and secretion of CSF
    E. Termination of REM sleep

15. Massaging the skin or applying an irritating substance to the skin can suppress the transmission of pain signals from the corresponding area of the body by suppressing the sensory fibers that transmit the pain signal. Which statement below best describes the statement?
    A. Release of encephalin from local neurons in the spinal cord
    B. Presynaptic and postsynaptic inhibition of serotonin C-type fibers
    C. Lateral inhibition of algogenic fibers by tactile fibers from adjacent areas of the skin
    D. Activation of neurons of the periaqueductal grey substance
    E. Release of endorphin from local neurons in the spinal cord

16. Which components of the somatic sensory system can be described as being responsible for perception or surface texture and shape discrimination and end in Brodmann areas 1 and 3b?
    A. Muscle proprioceptors
    B. Cutaneous mechanoreceptors
    C. Joint proprioceptors
    D. Stereogenesis
    E. Thermoreceptors

17. Which components of the somatic sensory system can be described as being responsible for perception of the shape and size of a grasped object and terminate in Brodmann area 2?
    A. Thermoreceptors
    B. Cutaneous mechanoreceptors
    C. Nociception
    D. Joint proprioceptors
    E. Muscle proprioceptors

18. Which components of the somatic sensory system can be described as being responsible for supplying information on position and direction of movement and terminate in Brodmann area 3a?
    A. Joint proprioceptors **B. Muscle proprioceptors**
    C. Nociception D. Thermoreceptors
    E. Cutaneous mechanoreceptors

19. Which of the following can be described as the tactile perception of the 3D shape of things using information from cells in Brodmann areas 2 and 3b?
    A. Nociception B. Somatic map
    C. Joint proprioceptors **D. Stereogenesis**
    E. Cutaneous mechanoreceptors

20. The second neuron of the appropriate sensory pathway connecting a free nerve termination in the left thumb with the somatosensory cortex travels in:
    A. The anterolateral homolateral spine
    B. The medial homolateral lemniscus
    C. The contralateral anterolateral spine
    D. The contralateral medial lemniscus
    E. The cerebellar reticulum beam

21. Considering that all motor and sensory reflex neural pathways are intact, which of the following elements will cause skeletal muscle contraction by means of its stimulation?

22. **A. Sensitive nerve endings type Ia**
    B. Sensitive nerve endings type Ib
    C. Ventromedial hypothalamus neurons
    D. Postganglionary vagal fibers
    E. None of the above

23. Considering that all the sensory, motor and reflex pathways are intact, which of the following structures can trigger a muscle contraction when stimulated?
   A. Alpha motor neurons
   B. Gamma motor neurons
   C. Annulospiral terminal
   D. Ia fiber
   E. All of the above options

24. Tendon reflexes show a stereotyped pattern of muscle contraction. Which of the following statements about the knee jerk, elicited in a clinical examination, is true?
   A. Golgi tendon organs in the quadriceps muscles discharge impulses to the spinal cord
   B. The nerve fibre from the muscle spindle synapses with the dendrites of α-motor neurons supplying the quadriceps muscles
   C. Signals in the spinal cord are transmitted to the thalamus
   D. The nerve impulses must pass through two synapses before the knee jerk can occur
   E. Inhibitory impulses are sent to the alpha-motor neurons supplying the gastrocnemius muscles

25. Considering that all motor and sensory reflex neural pathways are intact, which of the following elements will cause skeletal muscle contraction by means of its stimulation?
   A. Sensitive nerve endings type Ia
   B. Sensitive nerve endings type Ib
   C. Ventromedial hypothalamus neurons
   D. Postganglionary vagal fibers
   E. None of the above

26. There are two main motor pathways: the corticospinal tracts and the rubrospinal tract. Which of the following statements about the left corticospinal tract is true?
   A. It carries voluntary motor fibres
   B. It passes through Brodmann's areas
   C. Most of its fibres cross over to the right side in the pons
   D. Most of its fibres descend in the right side of the spinal cord as the anterior corticospinal tract
   E. Less than 20% of its fibres descend in the right side of the spinal cord as the lateral corticospinal tract

27. Which of the following sequences follows a pathway for proprioceptive information from the lower limb?
   A. Dorsal root ganglion cells ⇒ dorsal nucleus ⇒ dorsal spinocerebellar tract ⇒ superior cerebellar peduncle
   B. Clarke's column ⇒ ventral spinocerebellar tract ⇒ inferior cerebellar peduncle
   C. Dorsal root ganglion cells ⇒ dorsal spinocerebellar tract ⇒ nucleus Z ⇒ medial lemniscus ⇒ VPL nucleus
   D. Cuneate fasciculus ⇒ internal arcuate fibers ⇒ medial lemniscus ⇒ VPL nucleus
   E. All of the above answers are false

28. Parkinson's disease is a disorder of movement. Parkinson's disease is associated with which of the following?
   A. A reduction in striatal activity
   B. A reduction in nigrostrial neurons
   C. Reduced activity of cholinergic neurons
   D. A loss of GABA-ergic pathway
   E. A reduction in MPTP (1-methly-4-phenyl-1,2,5,6-tetrahydropyridine)-like substance

29. The basal ganglia are subcortical nuclei that lie deep within the white matter of the cerebral hemispheres. The basal ganglia consist of five connected structures that make up the extrapyramidal system: caudate nucleus, putamen, globus pallidus, subthalamus and substantia nigra. What is the role of substantia nigra?
   A. Intentional movement
   B. Pituitary secretion of prolactin
   C. Reward and motivation
   D. Sleep and being awake
   E. Working memory and cognitive tasks

30. The action of dopamine in the caudate nucleus and the putamen _____ the activity in the internal globus pallidus (GPi) as a consequence of _______.
   A. Reduces / the activation of the direct pathway and the inhibition of the indirect pathway
   B. Reduces / the inhibition of the direct pathway and the activation of indirect pathway
   C. Increases / the activation of the direct pathway and the inhibition of the indirect pathway
   D. Increases / the inhibition of the direct pathway and the activation of the indirect pathway
   E. Reduces / the inhibition of the direct and indirect pathways

31. A 75-year-old man is seen by a neurologist. The patient has an asymmetric resting tremor affecting his arms, rigidity and bradykinesia evolving over 1 year. Lying and standing blood pressure is normal and he has no balance problems. He has no other medical conditions. Levodopa is prescribed and there is good improvement. The patient is followed up over the next few years. What condition is this patient most likely to have?
   A. Ménière's disease
   B. Idiopathic Parkinson's disease
   C. Levodopa-induced dyskinesia
   D. Huntington's disease
   E. Intention tremor

32. The cerebellum is subdivided into the vestibulocerebellum, spinocerebellum and the cerebrocerebellum, each with a specific function. Which of the following are characteristic features associated with lesions in the vestibulocerebellum?
   A. Inability to stand upright without support
   B. Finger–nose incoordination
   C. Impaired articulation
   D. Increased muscle tone in the limbs
   E. Loss of joint position sense

33. The cerebellum is subdivided into the vestibulocerebellum, spinocerebellum and the cerebrocerebellum, each with a specific function. Which of the following are characteristic features of neocerebellar lesions?
   A. Tremor at rest
   B. Impaired 'heel-to-toe' walking
   C. Impaired ipsilateral 'heel-to-shin' test
   D. Aphonia
   E. Staggering gait

34. The lesion of which structure would cause extensional stiffness that would NOT be significantly altered by the severance of the dorsal roots:
   A. Lateral vestibular nucleus
   B. Anterior vermis of the cerebellar cortex
   C. Bulbar reticular formation (gigantocellular nucleus)
   D. Cortical afferents towards the pontine and bulbar reticular formation
   E. Cerebellar hemisphere cortex

35. In a person standing up straight, rotating the head to the right will:
   A. Activate the hair cells of the left channel and the right abducens nucleus
   B. Activate the hair cells of the right channel and the right abducens nucleus
   C. Activate the hair cells of the left channel and the left abducens nucleus
   D. Activate the hair cells of the right channel and the left abducens nucleus
   E. Result in vertical nystagmus

36. Consider a situation where a subject turns his or her head to the left on the axis of the neck. The movement begins when the chin is directly over the right shoulder and ends when it is directly over the left shoulder. Which of the following best describes the eye movements associated with this type of head rotation in a normal subject?
   A. As the head rotates, the eyes will move to the right and the saccadic movement of the eye will be to the left
   B. As the head rotates, the eyes will move in the same direction as the rotation of the head and the saccadic movement of the eye will be to the left
   C. As the head rotates, the eyes will move to the right and the saccadic movement of the eye will be to the right
   D. As the head rotates, the eyes will remain fixed within the orbits and the saccadic movement of the eye will be to the right
   E. None of the above is correct

37. A medical student is listening to his music collection whilst revising. In a hair cell, when the hair bundle is deflected towards the shortest stereocillium, which of the following statements is true?
   A. Transduction channels close
   B.Transduction channels open
   C. The tip links stretch
   D. The tip links break
   E. The cell depolarizes

38. In the right horizontal semicircular canal, in which relative direction will the endolymph move if the head is rotated rapidly in a clockwise direction?
   A. In clockwise direction
   B. In counterclockwise direction
   C. In ascending direction
   D. In descending direction
   E. Contrary to the movement of the endolymph in the left horizontal semicircular canal

39. Which of the following neurotransmitters is released by the gigantocellularis neurons of the reticular formation?
   A. Norepinephrine
   B. Serotonin
   C. Dopamine
   D. Acetylcholine
   E. None of the above

40. What type of brain wave pattern characterizes the EEG during the tonic phase of a tonic-clonic seizure?
   A. Large amplitude delta waves
   B. Theta waves
   C. High voltage and high frequency shock throughout the cortex
   D. Low amplitude alpha waves
   E. High voltage and high frequency shock in the focus region

41. Typical epileptic crises known as "petit mal" are characterized by:
   A. Tonic-clonic seizures
   B. A brief period of unconsciousness
   C. Uncontrolled muscle activity limited to one limb
   D. Fall due to loss of muscle tone
   E. All of the above options

42. 1.A medical student is having her elective in Kenya, where on safari she meets a wild and ferocious lion while walking in the plains. She is frightened, her heart rate increases and she runs away as fast as she can. According to the James-Lange theory, which of the following statements best describes the relationship between these events?
   A. You see the lion and are frightened. The fear increases your heart rate, helping you to run away faster
   B. You see the lion and are frightened. Your heart rate increases because you start to run
   C. Seeing the lion makes your heart beat faster and you start to run. You feel frightened because your heart is beating fast
   D. Seeing the lion makes you run. Your heart rate increases. Your fear is independent of your heart rate and behaviour
   E. You see the lion and start to run. You feel frightened and this makes your heart beat faster

43. In what brain structure could a lesion be located that is associated with the inability to correctly vocalize words without losing the understanding of the meaning of the written word and the idea transmitted by the word?
   A. The Broca's area
   B. The Wernicke's area
   C. The limbic amygdala
   D. The occipital lobe
   E. The thalamus

VIVA / SHORT QUESTION

1. What are the functions of functions of Glial cells?
Ans: Four types of glial cells in CNS: Astrocytes, Oligodendrocytes, Ependymal cells and Microglia. They form the mechanical matrix in which neurons are embedded, play metabolic and nutritive roles for neurons, help to regulate blood flow through the brain, act as a sink or source of ions, insulate axons and synapses and electrically isolate them from one another, phagocytose neural debris.

2. What is excitatory postsynaptic potential (EPSP)?
Ans: EPSP is the potential change in the postsynaptic membrane during synaptic transmission towards depolarization. EPSP is caused by opening of Na^+ or Ca^{++} ion channels in the postsynaptic membrane that results in influx of Na^+ or Ca^{++} and causes depolarization.

3. What is inhitatory postsynaptic potential (IPSP)?
Ans: IPSP is the potential of postsynaptic membrane is carried towards hyperpolarization. IPSP is produced by opening of Cl^- channels (Cl^- enters into the cells along the concentration gradient). Opening of K^+ cannels that result in K^+ efflux can produce IPSP. Closure of Na^+ or Ca^{++} channels also produce IPSP.

4. List the properties of synapse.
Ans: Law of Forward Conduction, Synaptic Delay, Law of Convergence and Divergence, Postsynaptic Potentials, Synaptic Inhibitions, Synaptic Facilitation, Summation, Occlusion, Habituation, Sensitization & Potentiation, Synaptic Plasticity

5. Define receptor.
Ans: Receptors are transducers that convert various forms of energy in the environment into action potentials in sensory neurons.

6. Classify receptor.
Ans:
i) Based on Function (exteroceptors, interoceptors, proprioceptors and teleceptors)
ii) Based on Adequate Stimulus (mechanoreceptors, thermoreceptors, nociceptors, chemoreceptors and photoreceptors)
iii) Based on Location (Superficial, Deep, Visceral)

7. List the properties of receptor.
Ans: Specificity, Adequate stimulus, Adaptation, Acuity, Intensity, Weber-Fechner law, Law of Projection, Doctrine of Specific Nerve Energy, Sensory Unit and Receptive Field, Recruitment of Sensory Unit

8. Name the ascending pathways?
Ans: Dorsal column pathways, Anterior spinothalamic tract, Lateral spinothalamic tract, and Other ascending pathways (Dorsal Spinocerebellar tract, Ventral Spinocerebellar tract), Spinoreticulothalamic tract, Spinocervicothalamic tract).

9. What are the sensations carried in the dorsal column pathway?
Ans: Fine touch, Vibration, Proprioception, Tactile localization, Tactile discrimination, Stereognosis.

10. What are the sensations carried in the spinothalamic tracts.
Ans: Anterior spinothalamic tract carries the sensation of crude touch, and lateral spinothalamic tract carries the sensation of pain and temperature.

11. What is dissociated anesthesia?
Ans: When the sensation of pain and temperature is lost with the preservation of touch, the condition is known as dissociated anesthesia. Seen in Syringomyelia, Intramedullary tumors.

12. What is Brown-Sequard Syndrome?
Ans: Hemisection of the spinal cord in injury to the spinal cord or in tumors of the spinal cord that affects only half of the cord
Sensory deficit: On the side of lesion, the fine-touch sensation, proprioceptive sensations and tactile discrimination are lost. On the opposite side, pain and thermal sensations are lost.
Motor deficit: There is also damage to corticospinal tract on the side of hemisection of spinal cord. This causes muscle weakness and spasticity of muscles of the same side of the body.

13. What is Rhomberg sign?
Ans: Inability to maintain a balanced standing position with feet together and eyes closed is called Romberg sign. This displays the lack of sense of position in both the legs. The patient should be tested in bare-foot.

14. What are the special characteristics of visceral pain?
Ans: Poorly localized, stimulus for elicitation of visceral pain is the distention of viscera, unpleasant, associated with autonomic symptoms like change in blood pressure, sweating, etc., causes muscle spasm and rigidity, shows referred pain.

15. What are the theories of referred pain?
Ans: Dermatomal theory, Convergence theory, Facilitation theory, Experience theory

16. What are the functions of Thalamus ?
Ans: Relay station for all somatic sensations, Relay center for all special sensations except olfaction, Arousal mechanisms, Subcortical Perception of Sensations, Motor Functions, Memory and Emotion, Synchronization of EEG, Sleep, Sensory Motor Coordination, Language and speech.

17. List the sensory cortical areas.
Ans: Primary Somatosensory Area I (SI), Primary Somatosensory Area II (SII), Somatosensory Association Cortex (Brodmann's area 5), Supplementary Sensory Pre-central gyrus (area 4), Cortical areas surrounding SII (area 7b).

18. List the functions of Muscle spindle.
Ans: Muscle spindles are receptors that are sensitive to stretch. When the muscle spindle is stretched, the sensory endings are distorted and action potential is generated in the afferent fibers. The frequency of afferent signal is proportional to the degree of stretching. Contraction of muscle inhibits the spindle and causes muscle relaxation.

19. List the functions of golgi tendon organ .
Ans: GTO provides the force feedback. GTO is activated by a strong muscle contraction and stimulates group Ib afferent fibers that terminate indirectly on α motor neurons via interneurons and cause muscle relaxation.

20. What are the Special Features of Withdrawal Reflex?
Ans: Protective Reflex, Pre-Potent, Local Sign, After-Discharge

21. Name the descending tracts.
Ans: Descending motor pathways have been traditionally classified into pyramidal and extrapyramidal tracts. Pyramidal tracts (Corticospinal tract), Extrapyramidal tracts (reticulospinal, vestibulospinal, rubrospinal, and tectospinal tracts)
Physiologically, descending pathways are divided into two: lateral system and medial system pathways.
Lateral System Pathways: Lateral corticospinal tract and rubrospinal tract.
Medial System Pathways: Reticulospinal tract, Vestibulospinal tract, Tectospinal tract, Anterior corticospinal tract

22. What arae the Features of UMN Paralysis
Ans: Increased muscle tone (spasticity), No muscle atrophy.Muscles are usually affected in groups, Tendon reflexes are exaggerated, Superficial reflexes are lost, Extensor planter response (Babinski's sign positive), No fascicular twitches, No denervation potential in EMG Normal nerve conduction studies.

23. What arae the Features of LMN Paralysis
Ans: Flaccid paralysis (muscles are hypotonic), Pronounced muscle atrophy, Individual muscles are affected depending on the muscles supplied by that particular nerve, Tendon reflexes are diminished or absent
Superficial reflexes are lost, Flexor planter response (Babinski's sign is not elicited), Involuntary movements like fascicular twitches are observed, Denervation potentials (fibrillation, fasciculation, and sharp waves) are seen in EMG, Nerve conduction is decreased or absent.

24. What are the reflexes integrated at the level of spinal cord?
Ans: Stretch reflex (Myotatic reflex), Inverse stretch reflex (Inverse myotatic reflex), Withdrawal reflex (Flexion reflex), Positive supporting reaction, Negative supporting reaction.

25. What are the reflexes integrated in the medulla?
Ans: Extensor rigidity, Tonic labyrinthine reflexes, Tonic neck reflexes

26. What are the reflexes integrated in the midbrain?
Ans: Labyrinthine Righting Reflex, Body on Head Righting Reflex, Neck Righting Reflex, Body on Body Righting Reflex, Limb Righting Reflex

27. What are the cortical motor areas?
Ans: Primary motor cortex, Pre-motor cortex, Supplementary motor area, Somatosensory cortex, Frontal eye field

28. What are the components of basal ganglia?
Ans: Caudate nucleus, putamen, globus pallidus, Subthalamic nucleus, and substantia nigra

29. What are the functions of basal ganglia?
Ans: Involved in planning and programming of motor activities, Controls posture, Inhibits stretch reflexes, Regulates subconscious gross movements, Cognitive functions, Coordination of impulses essential for skilled movements, Controls associated movements

30. What is the cause and features of Parkinson's disease?
Ans: Due to degeneration of dopaminergic neurons.
Hypokinetic Features: Akinesia, Bradykinesia, Decreased associated movements, Serpentine Stare
Hyperkinetic Movements: Rigidity, Tremor, Festinant gait, Micrographia

31. What is the treatment of Parkinson's disease?
Ans: Replacement of dopamine (Levodopa), Anticholinergics, MAO-B Inhibitors (Deprenyl), Transplantation of adrenal medulla, Implantation of fetal basal ganglia, Transplantation of glomus cells

32. What are the functional division of cerebellum?
Ans: Vestibulocerebellum, Spinocerebellum and Cerebrocerebellum

33. What are the functions of cerebellum?
Ans: Control of postural balance and equilibrium, Vestibulo-ocular reflex, Smoothening and coordination of movement, Control of posture, Control of skilled voluntary movements, Planning and programming of the movements, Control of muscle tone and stretch reflexes, Control of movements of same side of the body, Learning and improvement of motor skill, Prevents overshoot and damp movements, Eye ball movement, Vestibular functions.

34. What are the features of cerebellar disease?
Ans: No paralysis, No sensory deficit, Hypotonia, Ataxia (Drunken gait, Scanning speech, Dysmetria, Intention tremor, Rebound phenomenon, Adiadochokinesia, Decomposition of movement), Inability to carry out long-term adjustment in motor response, pendular knee jerk is elicited, nystagmus, Charcot's triad (nystagmus, intention tremor and scanning speech), Friedreich's Ataxia

SECTION XII- SPECIAL SENSES

MULTIPLE CHOICE QUESTIONS

1. Light from a distance has to fall on the retina for normal vision. Refractive errors occur when light from distant objects fails to focus on the retina. Which of the following is true of myopia (short-sightedness)?
   A. May be due to an abnormally short eyeball
   B. May be due to excessive curvature and divergence power of the cornea or lens
   C. Is associated with images formed behind the retina
   D. May be corrected using convex lenses
   E. Is often genetic in aetiology

2. Photoreceptors respond differently in the dark and in the light.When an individual with normal vision moves from a very bright to a very dark room, what change is likely to occur?
   A. The retina becomes less sensitive to light
   B. The changes in visual threshold occur more quickly than the reverse changes on moving from a very dark to a very bright room
   C. The initial changes in visual threshold are due to adaptation in the rods
   D. The later changes in visual threshold are due to adaptation of the cones
   E. The changes occur quicker if the individual had worn red-tinted glasses in the bright room

3. In retinal rods, retinal combines with protein 7-transmembrane opsin to form rhodopsin. When light acts on rhodopsin, all-trans-retinal becomes 11-cis-retinal and rhodopsin undergoes a conformational change. This induces stimulation of a G protein called transducin.How does a retinal rod hyperpolarize transducin?
   A. Transducin stimulates cyclic guanosine monophosphate phosphodiesterase.
   B. Transducin stimulates adenylate cyclase
   C. Transducin stimulates mitogen-activated protein kinase.
   D. Transducin stimulates phospholipase C.
   E. Transducin stimulates the Raf molecule.

4. Which of the following statements correctly explains the events that cause the change of the potential of the receptor in the photoreceptor stick during photoactivation?
   A. cGMP-dependent sodium channels on the outer segment of the rod open, causing hyperpolarization of the recipient
   B. Concentrations of cGMP increase, resulting in depolarization of the receptor
   C. Concentrations of cGMP increase, resulting in increased sodium entry into the outer segment of the rod and hyperpolarization of the receptor
   D. Concentrations of cGMP decrease, resulting in a decrease in sodium entry into the outer segment of the rod and the receptor becomes hyperpolarised
   E. None are correct

5. In the presence of light, the pigments in the retina undergo a sequence of events known as phototransduction. Which of the following events occur in the photosensitive pigments of the retina in the presence of light?
   A. Transducin (Gt1) is inhibited
   B. Conformal changes in the pigments occur
   C. Phosphodiesterase is inhibited
   D. Intracellular cAMP is increased
   E. Sodium channels are opened

6. Light intensity is signalled by optic nerve axons which synapse in the pretectum of the midbrain. To which nuclei do the pretectal axons relay to, and contain preganglionic parasympathetic neurones that run in the oculomotor nerves to the ciliary ganglia?
   A. Dentate nuclei **B. Edinger-Westphal nuclei**
   C. Lateral geniculate nuclei D. Lateral vestibular nuclei
   E. Pontine nuclei

7. The size of the pupils changes according to the amount of light entering the eye.Which of the following are neural pathways involved in the direct pupillary light reflex?
   A. The ganglion cells within the retina conduct impulses via the optic tracts to the lateral geniculate body
   B. The lateral geniculate body conducts impulses towards the superior cervical ganglion in the sympathetic chain
   C. The superior cervical ganglion conducts impulses towards the Edinger–Westphal nucleus
   D. The fibres from the Edinger–Westphal nucleus enter the oculomotor nerve and synapse in the ciliary ganglion
   E. Pre-ganglionic fibres from the ciliary ganglion supply the sphincter pupillae in the iris

8. Women in ancient Egypt used belladonna extract in their eyes for aesthetic reasons. Which of the following visual function declines would most likely affect them?
   A. Difficulty to see objects within hand reach
   B. Difficulty to see objects at a distance
   C. Difficulty to focus in low-light conditions
   D. Difficulty to move the eyes in a coordinated way
   E. None of the above

9. The oculomotor (cranial IIIr, trochlear (cranial IV) and abducens (cranial VI) nerves control eye movements. Which of the following statements about the medial longitudinal fasciculus (MLF) is true?
   A. It connects the oculomotor, trochlear and abducens nuclei
   B. It receives neural input from the trigeminal nuclei
   C. It is essential for balance
   D. A lesion in the MLF may result in failure of abduction of the ipsilateral eye
   E. A lesion in the MLF may result in nystagmus of the ipsilateral eye

10. Perception of the direction and characteristics of sound have to be conducted to the primary auditory cortex in the brain.The auditory nerve impulses in the acoustic nerve pass through which of the following to reach the primary auditory cortex?
    A. Contralateral cochlear nuclei in the medulla
    B. Ipsilateral vestibular nuclei
    C. Ipsilateral lateral geniculate body
    D. Contralateral medial geniculate body
    E. Ipsilateral superior colliculus

11. One of the two processes in hearing is localization of the sound source. Which of the following contribute to the effective localization of sound source?
    A. The left and the right side is partly due to the simultaneous arrival of stimulus in the two ears
    B. The left and the right side is partly due to the primary auditory cortex receiving signals produced by the stimuli only from the contralateral ear
    C. The left and the right side is partly due to the sound being louder on the side of the source
    D. The front and the back is partly due to the time difference between the arrival of stimulus in the two ears
    E. The front and the back is due to the time of arrival of the sound

12. Which of the following is the most likely result of a damage to the inner hair cells of the organ of Corti located from the middle of the basilar membrane to the helicotrema?
    A. Loss of ability to perceive high-frequency sounds
    B. Loss of ability to perceive loud sounds
    C. Loss of ability to perceive high-pitched sounds
    D. Loss of ability to perceive low and medium frequency sounds
    E. Loss of ability to discriminate the direction of sounds

13. What chemical properties must be at least partially present in a substance for it to be perceived by the olfactory system as an odor?
    A. Must be partially water soluble
    B. Must be partially liposoluble
    C. Must be volatile
    D. May be acidic or basic
    E. All of the above are correct

14. In which of the following structures does the first central synapse of the neurons that transmit the sensation of sweet taste occur?
    A. The nucleus of the vagus nerve
    B. The nucleus of the solitary tract
    C. The nucleus of the olfactory nerve
    D. The nucleus of the hypoglossal nerve
    E. The subthalamic nucleu

VIVA / SHORT QUESTION

1. What are the layers of retina?

   Ans: Layer of pigment epithelium, Layer of rods and cones, External limiting membrane, Outer nuclear layer, Outer plexiform layer, Inner nuclear layer, Inner plexiform layer, Layer of ganglion cells, Layer of nerve fibers, Internal limiting membrane.

2. What are the receptors for vision?

   Ans: rods (for daylight vision) and cones (for color vision)

3. What is fovea centralis?

   Ans: At the posterior pole of the eye, a small yellowish spot of about 1-2 mm in diameter is present, called the macula lutea. Its central part has a small depression of about 0.4 mm in diameter, called the fovea centralis. The fovea contains large number of tightly packed small sized cones. It is the most sensitive part of the retina having maximum visual acuity.

4. What is optic disc?

   Ans: The optic disc is an area in the retina devoid of the photoreceptors. It is located about 3 mm medial to the posterior pole of the eye. It is observed as a blind spot, while mapping the peripheral field of vision.

5. What is fundus?

   Ans: This is the posterior portion of the interior of the eye as seen through an ophthalmoscope. The fundus is the only region in the body where arterioles are readily visible. The progress of several systemic diseases like diabetes mellitus, hypertension and atherosclerosis that affect the vessel wall can be assessed by examining the changes in retinal blood vessels.

6. What is intraocular pressure (IOP) ?

   Ans: The IOP is 10-20 mmHg. Increased IOP causes glaucoma and in long-term leads to degeneration of the retina. IOP is measured by tonometry

7. What is the refractive power of eye?

   Ans: The eye has a total refractive power of 60 D; out of which 43 D is contributed by the cornea and only 17 D by lens.

8. What is the refractive power of lens?

   Ans: The refractive power of a lens is expressed in diopters (D), which is the reciprocal of the focal distance of a lens in meters. A lens with a focal length of one meter has a refractive power of 1/1= 1D. Similarly, lenses with focal lengths of 2m, 0.5m and 0.25 m have refractive powers of 0.5 D (1/2), 2 D (1/0.5), and 4D (1/0.25).

9. What is the accommodation?

   Ans: To focus an object present within 6 m, the eye has to increase its refractive power, a process called accommodation, in which the curvature of the lens is increased, the ciliary muscle contracts, and the suspensory ligaments relax.

10. What is the near point?

    Ans: It is defined as the nearest point to the eye, at which an object can be clearly seen. At this point, accommodation is exerted to its maximum. For a 30 yers adult, the near point is at about 13cm. The near point recedes throughout life. This gradual loss of accommodation is due to progressive loss of elasticity of the lens.

11. What is the near response?

    Ans: When an individual changes his gaze from a distant object to a near object, three changes occur in his eye. They are:

    i. Increase in curvature of the anterior surface of the lens (accommodation)

    ii. Convergence of the visual axes (as the eyeballs rotate medially)

    iii. Constriction of the pupil.

12. What is Myopia and how can it be corrected?

    Ans: It is a refractive error in which parallel rays of light from a distant object are brought into a focus in front of the retina when the accommodation is at rest. Myopia can be corrected by using spectacle with biconcave lens.

13. What is hypermetropia and how can it be corrected?

    Ans: It is a refractive error in which parallel rays of light from a distant object are brought into a focus behind the retina when the accommodation is at rest. It can be corrected by using spectacles with biconvex lens that converges the incident rays before they strike the cornea.

14. What is astigmatism and how can it be corrected?

    Ans: It is a refractive error in which parallel rays of light from a distant object cannot converge to a point focus on the retina due to unequal refraction at different meridians. It is corrected by using a cylindrical lens.

15. What is presbyopia and how can it be corrected?

    Ans: This is a physiological phenomenon seen at about the age of 40 years in which the near point of vision recedes beyond the normal reading or working distance due to progressive loss of plasticity of the lens. It is corrected by bifocal lenses (convex lens for near vision, and concave lens for distant vision).

16. What is phototransduction?

    Ans: When light strikes the eye, a hyperpolarizing potential is generated in the rods and cones, known as photoreceptor potential. The conversion of the light energy to neural signal by the visual pigments in the photoreceptors is known as phototransduction.

17. What is aisual acuity?

    Ans: Visual acuity is defined as the ability of the eye to identify two closely placed points as two distinct points. Visual acuity expresses the resolving power of the eye, that is, the extent to which the eye can perceive the details and contours of an object. Visual acuity is the function of the cones.

18. What is minimum separable distance?
Ans: The shortest distance, by which two objects can be separated and still be visualized as two different objects, is known as the minimum separable distance.

19. What are the factors affecting visual acuity?
Ans: i) Optical Factors: Curvature of the cornea, Curvature of the lens, Plasticity of the lens, Condition of the ciliary muscle and lens ligaments.
ii) Retinal Factors: Visual acuity is highest at the fovea, where cones are concentrated.
iii) Stimulus Factors: Size of the object, Distance of the object from eye, Color of the object, Contrast between the object and the background, Shape of its borders, Brightness of the object, Duration for which the object remains in view.

20. What are the tests for visual acuity?
Ans: For distant vision by Snellen's chart; near vision by Jaeger's chart.

21. What is visual field?
Ans: The area of the external world that can be seen when the gaze is fixed is known as the visual field of that eye.

22. What is binocular vision?
Ans: Viewing an object as a single one with both eyes is called binocular vision. When a person looks at an object with both eyes, the light rays coming from the object stimulate both the retinas. The action potentials transmitted by the neural pathways from both retinas get fused at the visual cortex, so that the brain perceives them as single image.

23. What are the corresponding points?
Ans: The two points on the retinas on which the light rays from an object fall simultaneously to make binocular vision possible, are known as corresponding points.

24. What is bitemporal (heteronymous) hemianopia?
Ans: Lesion of optic chiasm damages the nasal fibers from both eyes and produces bitemporal (heteronymous) hemianopia.

25. What is homonymous hemianopia?
Ans: Lesion of optic tract damages ipsilateral temporal fibers and contralateral nasal fibers resulting in homonymous hemianopia. This usually occurs in tumors of anterior pituitary, a feature of acromegaly.

26. What is macular sparing?
Ans: Lesion of occipital cortex damages ipsilateral temporal fibers and contralateral nasal fibers with macular sparing, which occurs as the macular fibers project separately in the visual cortex, and they have a much larger representation compared to rest of the retina.

27. What is Light adaptation?
Ans: When a person suddenly moves from a dimly lighted area to broad daylight, the pupil constricts and the amount of light entering the retina is reduced. This is known as light adaptation. Light adaptation takes about 5 minutes.

28. What is the mechanism of light adaptation?
Ans: Two mechanisms: Neural and Chemical.
Neural Adaptation: Following a light stimulus, the sensitivity of retinal photoreceptors decreases
Chemical Adaptation: In bright light, rhodopsin is rapidly converted to all-trans-retinal and opsin. Due to this bleaching, rod responsiveness decreases considerably.

29. What is the mechanism of dark adaptation?
Ans: If a person stays for some time in bright sunlight and then moves into a dimly lighted room, the pupil dilates to allow the maximum possible light through the eye to have optimal vision. This is known as dark adaptation. Dark adaptation occurs in about 20 minutes.

30. What is night blindness?
Ans: Vitamin A is required for the synthesis of retinine. So, vitamin A deficiency adversely affects the dark adaptation ability, the condition known as night blindness, in which the person has impaired vision in the evening and dim light.

31. What is the pathway of light reflex?
Ans: The pupillary constriction occurring in the stimulated eye is called direct light reflex and in the other eye is called consensual light reflex.
Afferent pathway: The first order neurons from the retinal ganglion cells project to the pre-tectal nucleus; from here the second order neurons start and proceed to the mid-brain Edinger-Westphal nucleus.
Efferent pathway: The parasympathetic fibers of the oculomotor nerve form the first order neurons that originate from mid-brain Edinger-Westphal nucleus and project to the ciliary ganglion. The second order neurons start from here and innervate the sphincter pupillae.

32. What is the pathway of accommodation reflex?
Ans: The pupils of both eyes constrict on looking at a near object; this is called accommodation reflex.
Afferent pathway: The first order neurons from the retinal ganglion cells project to the LGB; from here, the second order neurons start and project to the area 17, from where the third order neurons start and proceed to the mid-brain Edinger-Westphal nucleus.
Efferent pathway: From the striate cortex via the occipito mesencephalic pathway, impulse travels to the oculomotor nerve nucleus and then to the sphincter pupillae, ciliary muscle and medial rectus.

33. What is Argyll Robertson Pupil?
Ans: The light reflexes (both direct and consensual) are lost, but accommodation reflex is present. This is the classical pupillary abnormality in neurosyphilis.

34. What are the primary colors and complementary color?
Ans: Primary colors: red, green and blue.
Complementary color. When any color is mixed with its complementary color, the mixture appears white. For example, purple and green, orange and blue, yellow and dark blue are complementary colors.

35. What are the theories of color vision?
Ans: Two theories: Pigment theory and Opponent theory.
Pigment theory (Young-Helmholtz theory): There are the three types of cones (red, green and blue) and each has a pigment with a different absorbance spectrum. The visual cortex compares the relative frequency of action potentials in the activated cone pathways and deciphers the wavelength and thereby, makes out the color.
Opponent theory (Hering's theory of color vision): There is no greenish-red or bluish-yellow color. The red and green colors oppose each other, and the blue and yellow colors are opposed. The ganglion cells, the cells of the LGB and the neurons of the visual cortex show color-opponent property.

36. What are the Types of color blindness ?
Ans:
i) Trichromats: All three-cone systems present , but one of the cone systems is defective. This is the most common type. It can present as Deuteranomaly (most common), Protanomaly or Tritanomaly
ii) Dichromats: These are individuals with two-cone systems and the third cone system is absent. They present as Deuteranopia (most common), Protanopia or Tritanopia.
iii) Monochromats: These are individuals with only one cone system present. Thus, they cannot appreciate any color, because minimum two cone systems are required to appreciate a color. They see only black and white and shades of gray.

37. What are the Tests for color blindness ?
Ans: Ishihara Chart, Edridge-Green Lantern Test, Holmgren's Wool-Matching Test

38. What is nystagmus ?
Ans: The involuntary, rhythmical, oscillatory movement of the eyeball is known as nystagmus.

39. What are the functions of the middle ear?
Ans: i) Receives sound waves from the external ear by the tympanic membrane
ii) Transmission of sound waves to the inner ear through the tympanic membrane and the ossicular chain.
iii) Amplification of sound waves:
iv) Equalization of air pressure through the eustachian tube.
v) Protects against prolonged, loud sound by activation of tympanic reflex.

40. What is normal threshold for hearing?
Ans: The threshold of hearing is 0 dB at 1000 Hz for a normal young adult in a noise free environment. Normal convrsation occurs at 60 dB.

41. What is masking?
Ans: The hearing threshold for a given sound increases in the presence of background sounds or noise. This phenomenon is known as masking.

42. What is air conduction?
Ans: From the tympanic membrane, sound waves are also transmitted through the air of the middle ear cavity and vibrate the secondary tympanic membrane to reach the perilymph of the scala tympani. This is known as air conduction.

43. What is bone conduction?
Ans: From the environment, sound waves get mechanically transmitted through the bones and reach the inner ear. Bone conduction is better appreciated when a vibrating tuning fork is placed on the bone of the skull, especially the mastoid process. It is used to diagnose hearing loss due to defective transmission of sound waves through the external and middle ear.

44. What is the receptor for hearing?
Ans: Hair cells

45. What is the mechanism of depolarization of hair cells ?
Ans:
i) When the shorter stereocilia bend toward the taller stereocilia, the cation channels open, allowing entry of K^+ into the hair cell
ii) The resulting depolarization causes opening of voltage-gated Ca^{+2} channels at the base of the hair cell.
iii) Increased cytoplasmic calcium concentration causes exocytosis of vesicles.
iv) This results in release of glutamate into the synaptic cleft producing action potentials in the afferent nerve fibers.

46. What is conduction deafness?
Ans: Conduction deafness occurs due to impaired transmission or amplification of sound to the cochlea due to disease of the external or middle ear.

47. What are the causes of conduction deafness?
Ans: i) Blockade of external auditory canal by impaction of wax, or foreign bodies or tumor of the auditory canal.
ii) Thickening of the tympanic membrane following repeated middle ear infections.
iii) Acute and chronic otitis media
Immobility of the ossicles, e.g. otosclerosis.
Destruction of the auditory ossicles.
vi) Eustachian tube obstruction

48. What is otosclerosis?
Ans: When the stapes is fixed to the oval window in an abnormally rigid manner, it is known as otosclerosis.

49. What is sensorineural deafness?
Ans: This occurs as a result of diseases of the cochlea or of the 8th

cranial nerve.

50. What is Meniere's disease?

Ans: Meniere's disease is characterized by episodic vertigo, deafness and tinnitus.

51. What are the causes of sensorineural deafness?

Ans:

i) Toxic degeneration of the hair cells caused by chronic treatment with drugs such as streptomycin, kanamycin, gentamycin
ii) Senile degeneration of the hair cells e.g. presbycusis
iii) Damage to the outer hair cells by prolonged exposure to loud noise
iv) Tumors of the vestibulocochlear nerve
v) Trauma or fracture of the base of the skull
vi) Labyrinthitis
vii) Meniere's disease

52. What is presbycusis?

Ans: There occurs gradual cumulative loss of hair cells and neurons due to effect of aging. This is known as presbycusis. It is seen in about one-third of population over 75.

53. What are the hearing tests?

Ans: Rinne's test, Weber's test, and Swabach's test.

54. What is vomeronasal organ?

Ans: In rodents and other mammals, another patch of olfactory mucus membrane is present along the nasal septum, called vomeronasal organ.

55. What are the cortical olfactory areas?

Ans: Piriform cortex, amygdala, entorhinal cortex, anterior olfactory nucleus, septum, hypothalamus, frontal cortex.

56. What are the types of taste sensations?

Ans: Sweet, salty, sour, bitter and umami.

SECTION XIII- INTEGRATED PHYSIOLOGY

MULTIPLE CHOICE QUESTIONS

1. The skin is the largest organ in the body and has a number of important functions. Which of the following changes occurs in the skin when the body temperature increases?
   A. The hairs become more erect
   B. The number of melanocytes decreases
   C. The secretion from sweat glands increases
   D. Blood flow to the skin decreases
   E. The secretion from sebaceous glands decreases

2. A 33-year-old woman walks through the desert. The temperature is 38.9 °C and the relative humidity is 68%.Which of the following heat loss mechanisms is most effective in this woman?
   A. Conduction towards the air
   B. Conduction towards objects
   C. Evaporation
   D. Radiation
   E. Convection

3. A diver explores a lava flow underwater. The water temperature is 39.4 °C. Which of the following groups of heat loss mechanisms is effective when this man swims in the water at that temperature? EvaporationRadiationConvectionConductionANo No NoYesBNo NoNoNoCNo YesNo YesDNo YesNoYesEYesYesYesYes
   A. Option A **B. Option B** C. Option C
   D. Option D E. Option E

4. A 29-year-old male is sitting naked in a room at 21.7 °C, with low humidity. He is 185 cm tall and weighs 96 kg (body mass index = 26.3). Through which of the following mechanisms is the maximum amount of body heat most likely to be lost?
   A. Conduction towards the air
   B. Conduction towards objects
   C. Evaporation
   D. Radiation
   E. Condensation

5. A 27-year-old man working on an Alaskan gas pipeline in winter produces heat through a non-shivering thermogenesis mechanism activated by the stress of cold. Which of the following best describes the mediator of non-shivering thermogenesis?
   A. Cortisol
   B. Parasympathetic nervous system
   C. Substance P
   D. Sympathetic nervous system
   E. Thyroxine

6. Environmental conditions can affect the control of human core body temperature, normally maintained between 36oC and 38oC. What factor in tropical countries can significantly impair the effectiveness of sweating as a mechanism for the control of body temperature?
   A. Humidity may reach 100%
   B. A lack of safe, clean drinking water leads to dehydration
   C. Increased storm activity reduces the number of direct sunlight hours
   D. High-intensity sunlight damages the skin surface, including sweat pores
   E. Vaccinations often received before travel impair thermoregulation

7. The temperature setpoint in the hypothalamus normally averages 37 °C. Which of the following factors can alter that level for core temperature control? Cutaneous temperature..Pyrogens... Antipyretics...Thyroxine...ANoYesYesNo BNoYesYes YesC YesYesYesYes DYesNoNoYe sEYesYes YesNo
   A. Option A B. Option B C. Option C
   D. Option D **E. Option E**

8. Which of the following heat loss mechanisms occurs in a normal person when the ambient temperature is 40.6 °C and the relative humidity is less than 20%?
   A. Conduction
   B. Convection
   C. Evaporation
   D. Radiation
   E. Irradiation

9. Which of the following best describes the mechanism through which sympathetic stimulation helps limit weight gain in an obese adult?
   A. A decrease in plasma leptin
   B. An increase in blood flow
   C. Brown fat metabolism
   D. Non-shivering thermogenesis
   E. Shivering thermogenesis

10. A healthy 20-year-old medical student undergoes an exercise stress test. Which of the following groups of changes could be expected in his skeletal muscle during exercise? Vascular resistance Capillary hydrostatic pressure Lymphatic flow Option 1 ↑ ↑ ↑ Option 2 ↑ ↑ ↓ Option 3 ↑ ↓ ↓ Option 4 ↑ ↓ ↑ Option 5 ↓ ↓ ↓ Option 6 ↓ ↓ ↑ Option 7 ↓ ↑ ↑ Option 8 ↓ ↑ ↓
    A. Option 1 B. Option 2 C. Option 3
    D. Option 5 **E. Option 7** F. Option 6
    G. Option 7 H. Option 8

11. A 25-year-old healthy medical student undergoes an exercise stress test in a gym. Which of the following groups of physiological changes would be most likely in your skeletal muscle during exercise: Arteriole diameter Adenosine concentration Tissue metabolism Option 1 ↑ ↑ ↑ Option 2 ↑ ↓ ↑ Option 3 ↑ ↓ ↓ Option 4 ↑ ↑ ↓ Option 5 ↓ ↓ ↓ Option 6 ↓ ↑ ↓ Option 7 ↓ ↑ ↑ Option 8 ↓ ↓ ↑

A. Option 1 B. Option 2 C. Option 3
D. Option 4 E. Option 5 F. Option 6
G. Option 7 H. Option 8

12. A healthy 40-year-old male has been doing maximum exercise for 15 minutes. Which of the following situations is more likely?
    A. Arteriolar resistance in the gastrointestinal bed increased by 200%
    B. Cerebral blood flow decreased by 50% compared to normal
    C. Heart rate has not changed
    D. Cardiac output increases by 5%
    E. Pressure in the right atrium increases to 10 mmHg

13. During exercise, a process of anticipatory increases in heart rate and oxygen supply is achieved before an increase is actually required. Of what is this process an example?
    A. Positive feedback
    B. Negative feedback
    C. Physiological anticipation
    D. Athletic adaptation
    E. Feedforward mechanism

14. The cardiovascular system has to adjust to changing demands for oxygen during exercise. Which one of the following significant changes would you expect to occur during exercise in a physically fit individual?
    A. Cardiac output decreases
    B. Peripheral resistance increases
    C. Diastolic pressure increases
    D. Blood arterioles in the muscles dilate
    E. Venous return decreases

15. During exercise, ventilation and oxygen consumption increase. Of the following factors, which significantly contributes to the increase in ventilation rate immediately before and during vigorous exercise?
    A. Reduction in arterial carbon dioxide (pCO2) level
    B. Afferent impulses from muscle and joint proprioceptors
    C. Reduced sensitivity of chemoreceptors to carbon dioxide
    D. Fluctuations: increase in arterial oxygen (pO2) level
    E. Reduced production of lactic acid

16. In normal people, the pulmonary blood flow when exercising in a biped position, if compared to when they are standing motionless, is:
    A. More distributed to the lower lung than to the upper lung
    B. More distributed to the top of the lung than to the lower lung
    C. Almost evenly distributed between the upper and lower parts of the lung
    D. Too variable to determine
    E. All of the above answers are false

17. Which of the following vascular beds suffers maximum vasoconstriction in a person who is finishing running 8 km?
    A. Cerebral
    B. Coronary
    C. Exercise muscle
    D. Intestinal
    E. Skin

18. Continuous workout on a treadmill results in a significant increase in skeletal muscle blood flows. As the most likely explanation for the increase in muscle blood flow, what change in concentrations of metabolites in muscle tissue is unsuspected and justifies such an increase? Carbon dioxide pH Adenosine Option 1↑↑↑Option 2↑↓↑Option 3↑↓↓Option 4↑↑↓Option 5↓↓↓Option 6↓↑↓Option 7↓↑↑Option 8↓↓↑
    A. Option 1 **B. Option 2** C. Option 3
    D. Option 4 E. Option 5 F. Option 6
    G. Option 7 H. Option 8

19. Which of the following sequences correctly indicates the degree of daily energy expenditure in a normal person, being 1 = the metabolism during sleep, 2 = lying down and 3 = sitting?
    A. 1 = 2 > 3 B. 1 < 2 = 3 C. 1 > 2 > 3
    D. 3 = 2 = 1 **E. 3 > 2 > 1** F. 3 > 2 > 1

VIVA / SHORT QUESTION

Integrative Physiology including Temperature Regulation, Exercise Physiology and Yoga

1. What are the functions of skin?
   Ans: Mechanical protection against infection; Temperature regulation; Sensory organs; Synthesis of 7-dehydrocholesterol; Contributes to central blood volume by cutaneous vasoconstriction; Water and electrolyte balance; Protection from UV rays; Skin plays a crucial role in nonspecific defence of the body; Route for drug administration; Diagnosis of skin diseases, many systemic diseases, detection of egree of anemia, jaundice and cyanosis; Beauty of the Body.

2. What are the mechanisms of heat production?
   Ans: At rest, heat production depends on basal metabolic activity, muscular activity, specific dynamic action of food and nonshivering thermogenesis.

3. What is specific dynamic action (SDA) of food?
   Ans: The, metabolic rate and thus, the heat production increases by about 15% after a meal. This is called SDA of food or thermic effect of food, which lasts for several hours after food intake. SDA is maximum for protein.

4. What is Nonshivering thermogenesis?
   Ans: Hormones such as catecholamines and thyroxine increase body metabolism. Therefore, these hormones contribute to basal heat production. This is called nonshivering thermogenesis.

5. What are the mechanisms of heat gain from the environment?
   Ans: From environment, body gains heat if environmental temperature is more than body temperature, and vice versa when environmental temperature is less. Heat gain from environment occurs by radiation, conduction and convection. Heat gain also occurs by means of ingestion of hot food and drinks and breathing hot air in hot climate.

6. What are the mechanisms of heat dissipation?
   Ans: Heat is lost from body through skin (cutaneous heat loss), lungs (pulmonary heat loss) and excretory organs (excretory heat loss). From skin, heat is dissipated into the atmosphere by means of radiation, conduction, convection and evaporation.

7. What is insensible water loss?
   Ans: Diffusion of fluid from the body to epidermis occurs continuously, which is evaporated from the body surface, even in the absence of external sweating. This is called perspiration or insensible water loss. It is not sensed by the body as sweating does not occur. It usually does not depend on external conditions. It accounts for loss of about 400 kcal heat per day.

8. What are the thermoreceptors?
   Ans: Thermal sensors are thermoreceptors respond to changes in local temperature. The cutaneous thermoreceptors inform body about thermal condition of the external environment. The hypothalamic thermoreceptors inform CNS about the body's internal thermal condition.

9. What are the hypothalamic structures for tempertaure regulation?
   Ans: Three categories: sensor neurons, heat-loss neurons and heat production neurons.
   Sensor neurons: These are hypothalamic thermoreceptors that are located in anterior hypothalamus.
   Heat-loss Neurons: Neurons that on activation induce loss of heat are located in anterior hypothalamus and preoptic area.
   Heat-production Neurons: The neurons that on stimulation activate mechanisms that prevent loss of heat and produce internal heat are located in posterior hypothalamus.

10. What are the mechanisms activated by heat?
    Ans: Mechanisms that promote heat loss and the mechanisms that reduce heat production.

11. What are the responses that promote heat loss?
    Ans: Cutaneous vasodilation, sweating and increased breathing.

12. What are the responses that reduce heat production?
    Ans: Loss of appetite and reduced physical activity.

13. What are the responses activated by cold?
    Ans: On exposure to cold environment, body tries to elevate its temperature by heat gain by processes that promote heat production and the processes that reduce heat loss.

14. What are the responses that promote heat production?
    Ans: Shivering and nonshivering thermogenesis, increased physical activity and increased intakes.

15. What are the responses that reduce heat loss?
    Ans: Cutaneous vasoconstriction, piloerection and change in body posture (curling up of the body)

16. What are the responses in heat acclimatization?
    Ans: Reduction in heart rate, Sweating rate becomes high and the higher sweat rate remains for sustained period, Reduction in the level of core and skin temperature during exercise, Sweat glands conserve sodium by secreting sweat with less sodium.

17. What are the responses in cold acclimatization?
    Ans: Cold-induced vasodilation occurs, which increases cutaneous blood flow, observed mainly in areas rich in arteriovenous anastomoses as in hands and feet, vasoconstriction alternating with vasodilation occurs in succession.

18. What are the features of heat stroke?
Ans: Heat stroke is characterized by high core temperature, neurological deficits, convulsion and/or loss of consciousness. Damage to kidney, liver and skeletal muscle are usual complications. Patient rapidly becomes comatose. The skin is dry and body temperature is usually above 106°F

19. What are the causes of heat stroke?
Ans: Hyperthermia, state of physical exercise, release of endotoxin from bacterial flora
In classical heatstroke, a very high environmental heat supersedes thermoregulatory mechanisms of the body.
In exertional heatstroke, exertion in a high ambient temperature accelerates production of metabolic heat.

20. What is the treatment of heat stroke?
Ans: Rapid reduction in body temperature, which is effectively accomplished by immersion of the body in cold water. Prompt hydration and maintenance of a patent airway prevents complications to develop.

21. What is malignant hyperthermia?
Ans: Very high increase in body temperature that usually occurs on exposure to anesthetics or depolarizing neuromuscular blockers. The plasma calcium concentration rises abnormally that severely activates myosin ATPase activity, increasing core temperature.
Treatment is by immediate use of dantrolene sodium that decreases the release of calcium from the sarcoplasmic reticulum

22. What is hypothermia?
Ans: On prolonged exposure to severely cold environment or proionged immersion in cold water body temperature decreases. When body temperature is less than 25°C, decreased body metabolism, enzymatic activity, slowing of heart and respiration, and slowing reflex activities, and in severe cases loss of consciousness occurs, which may further lead to death.

23. What are the respiratory changes during exercise?
Ans: Increase in both rate and depth of respiration and increased O^2 uptake by the lungs arterial pO^2 and pCO^2 are maintained almost at the normal level even during the strenuous exercise, as hyperventilation removes excess of CO^2 produced during exercise.

24. What are the cardiovascular changes during exercise?
Ans:
i) Increase in the cardiac output due to increase in both heart rate and stroke volume,
ii) Increase in the skeletal muscle blood flow,
iii) Redistribution of blood flow in the body: Vasoconstriction in visceral and cutaneous vascular bed and vasodilation in coronary and cerebral circulation.
iv) Changes in blood pressure: Increase in systolic blood pressure always. Increase in diastolic pressure in mild to moderate exercise, decrease in diastolic pressure in moderate to severe exercise.
v) Changes in blood volume. Effective circulating volume falls due to increase in capillary filtration, sweating and evaporation

25. What are the hormones that stimulate growth?
Ans: Growth hormone, insulin-like growth factor, thyroxine, gonadal hormones and insulin.

26. What are the differences between pituitary dwarf and thyroid dwarf?
Ans: Pituitary dwarf: Deficient secretion of GH or GHRH early in life leads to pituitary dwarf. Mental development remains apparently normal, but reproductive functions are severely impaired.
Thyroid dwarf: Deficiency of thyroid hormone at childhood causes cretinism. Mental development is grossly impaired though reproductive functions are apparently normal.

27. What are the benefits of surya namaskar?
Ans:
1. Improves flexibility of joints, and suppleness of musculoskeletal system.
2. Modulate blood flow to visceral organs and improve their functions.
3. Controls secretion from endocrine glands and therefore profoundly influences body metabolisms.
4. Improves insulin secretion and sensitivity, beneficial in diabetes.
5. Improves thyroid secretion and therefore greatly improve metabolisms.
6. Improves exocrine secretions, liver functions, GI motility and secretions.
7. Reduces fat in the abdomen and pelvic regions.
8. Increases blood flow to brain and improves memory, learning, general intelligence.
9. Improves cardiovascular functions, decreases blood pressure.
10. Improves autonomic balance and functions of internal organs.